KS3

SUCCESS

VISUAL REVISION GUIDE

QUESTIONS & ANSWERS

QUESTIONS & ANSWERS

ICT

Sean O'Byrne

CONTENTS

Homework Diary 4

Progress Plotter 5

WHAT IS ICT? 6

ICT IN SOCIETY 8

HARDWARE 10

SOFTWARE 12

DATA AND INFORMATION 14

SOURCES OF INFORMATION 16

DATA AND FILES 18

GRAPHICS AND SOUND 20

DATABASES 22

DATA CAPTURE FORMS 24

STRUCTURING DATA 26

VALIDATION AND VERIFICATION 28

QUERIES, INDEXES AND FILTERS 30

REPORTS 32

SEARCH ENGINES 34

AUTOMATIC DATA ENTRY 36

DATA MISUSE AND DAMAGE 38

DATA PRIVACY AND PROTECTION 40

SYSTEMS DEVELOPMENT 1 42

SYSTEMS DEVELOPMENT 2 44

WORD PROCESSING 46

DESKTOP PUBLISHING 48

SPREADSHEETS 1 50

SPREADSHEETS 2 52

SPREADSHEETS 3 54

MODELS AND SIMULATIONS 56

DATA-LOGGING 58

PROGRAMMING AND CONTROL 60

MULTIMEDIA 62

PRESENTATIONS 64

NETWORKS 66

THE INTERNET 68

E-MAIL 70

Homework Diary

TOPIC	SCORE
What is ICT?	/40
ICT in society	/33
hardware	/42
software	/33
data and information	/28
sources of information	/36
data and files	/31
graphics and sound	/30
databases	/27
data capture forms	/25
structuring data	/26
validation and verification	/27
queries, indexes and filters	/30
reports	/23
search engines	/29
automatic data entry	/30
data misuse and damage	/28
data privacy and protection	/30
systems development 1	/30
systems development 2	/34
word processing	/35
desktop publishing	/29
spreadsheets 1	/26
spreadsheets 2	/26
spreadsheets 3	/24
models and simulations	/31
data-logging	/33
programming and control	/29
multimedia	/30
presentations	/30
networks	/32
the Internet	/27
e-mail	/27

Progress Plotter

Once you have completed a unit, and filled in your score on the Homework Diary opposite, use this Progress Plotter to chart your success! Fill in the boxes with your score for each unit and watch your results get better and better.

	Nearly all right – excellent work!	More than half – good, but keep trying	Less than half – room for improvement	Under 5 – needs more work
What is ICT?				
ICT in society				
hardware				
software				
data and information				
sources of information				
data and files				
graphics and sound				
databases				
data capture forms				
structuring data				
validation and verification				
queries, indexes and filters				
reports				
search engines				
automatic data entry				
data misuse and damage				
data privacy and protection				
systems development 1				
systems development 2				
word processing				
desktop publishing				
spreadsheets 1				
spreadsheets 2				
spreadsheets 3				
models and simulations				
data-logging				
programming and control				
multimedia				
presentations				
networks				
the Internet				
e-mail				

WHAT IS ICT?

M Choose just one answer, a, b, c or d.

1 **Digital data**
   a) is stored as 0s and 1s
   b) has to be stored on disks
   c) is only used by computers
   d) can only be used for numbers.

2 **Flash memory is used to**
   a) process data
   b) store data until the power is switched off
   c) store data that can't be erased
   d) store data for as long as it is wanted.

3 **A microwave oven is controlled by a computer processor. What is the output from this computer processor?**
   a) the temperature selected
   b) the time taken
   c) a signal to turn the microwaves on
   d) dinner

4 **Mr Carpenter is a teacher. He uses a computer system to do his class register.**
   Which of these is most likely to be an input to this computer system?
   a) whether Jack is present today or not
   b) the total class attendances for the week
   c) the number of latecomers in the year
   d) the number of holiday absences in the year

5 **The school secretary keeps pupil records on a computer system. They are stored for the future. This storage is most likely to be**
   a) in the computer's main memory
   b) in the computer's processor
   c) on a hard disk
   d) on paper.

   Score   ...... /5

Q Answer all parts of all questions.

1 George wants to paint his house but doesn't know how many rooms he can afford to decorate. He uses his computer to find out.

   a) Give two inputs that he will need to give to the computer.

   ....(2 marks)

   b) Give two outputs that the computer will produce.

   ....(2 marks)

   c) Give two examples of processes that will have to happen.

   ....(2 marks)

2 Name three gadgets or appliances in your home that have computers or processors inside them.

   ....(3 marks)

3 Explain how advances in ICT have made cars more reliable.

   ....(2 marks)

Q | **Continued**

4 Computers are very versatile.
Explain how they can be made to do so many different things.

.... (2 marks)

Score .... /13

E

This is an exam-style question. Answer all parts of the question.

Mel wants to buy a ticket for a concert.
She phones the booking office to find out what tickets are available.

1 What information must she give to the booking office clerk when enquiring?

.... (2 marks)

2 What output will the booking clerk get from the computer?

.... (2 marks)

3 Mel decides to buy two tickets over the phone. What extra information must she give to the booking clerk?

.... (3 marks)

4 The booking office sends Mel the tickets. Describe two ways that the office can use ICT systems to get the tickets produced and sent to Mel.

.... (2 marks)

5 Mel enjoys the concert so much she decides she wants to play the same music at home.
   a) Describe two ways she can get hold of the music using digital technology.

.... (2 marks)

   b) Explain why digital technology is a good way to store music.

.... (2 marks)

   c) Explain how digital technology can be a threat to the music industry.

.... (3 marks)

6 Identify four other ways that Mel could use digital technology for entertainment.

.... (4 marks)

7 After the concert, Mel needs to get a taxi to go home. How can digital technology help her to do this?

.... (2 marks)

Score .... /22

TOTAL SCORE   /40

For more help on this topic see KS3 ICT Success Guide pages 4–5

ICT IN SOCIETY

M **Choose just one answer, a, b, c or d.**

1 Hospitals have machines controlled by computers that can look inside the body without harming it.
These systems are known as
a) CAD
b) CAM
c) CAL
d) CAT.

2 Which of these holds the most data?
a) CD
b) DVD
c) floppy disk
d) memory stick

3 Which of these is not a form of digital communication?
a) ADSL
b) standard telephone
c) satellite TV
d) ISDN

4 Which of these is a result of more computers being used at work?
a) most people get paid more
b) jobs become more secure
c) people change jobs more often
d) people don't work so hard

5 When using a cash machine, which of these is a correct sequence of actions?
a) insert card, enter PIN, choose service
b) enter PIN, insert card, withdraw cash
c) choose service, enter PIN, insert card
d) choose service, enter PIN, withdraw cash

Score .... /5

Q **Answer all parts of all questions.**

1 Give two reasons why most mobile phones use digital signals?

.... (2 marks)

2 Explain why health services do not yet have an efficient IT system.

.... (2 marks)

3 Give three ways that a teacher might use ICT to help with work.

....

.... (3 marks)

4 Give two advantages of communicating using digital rather than old-fashioned analogue technology.

.... (2 marks)

5 Give two ways that a doctor in general practice might use ICT to help with his or her work.

.... (2 marks)

Score .... /11

E **This is an exam-style question. Answer all parts of the question.**

Jack is an editor. He used to go to his employer's office each day, but now he works from home most of the time.

1 Explain how Jack's employers benefit from Jack's working at home.

.... (2 marks)

2 Explain why Jack is happy about working from home.

.... (2 marks)

3 Give two disadvantages of working from home.

....

.... (2 marks)

4 Apart from a computer, what other IT resources will Jack need at home in order to send work to the office?

....

.... (3 marks)

Jack gets paid for his work by bank credit transfer. He can manage his account from his computer at home.

5 State three other services that the bank can provide for Jack by using its IT systems.

....

....

.... (3 marks)

6 Describe a danger that Jack might face by using on-line banking.

.... (2 marks)

7 Give three reasons why computers are so useful to banks.

....

....

.... (3 marks)

Score ...... /17

TOTAL SCORE   /33

For more help on this topic see KS3 ICT Success Guide pages 6–7

HARDWARE

M | Choose just one answer, a, b, c or d.

1 A picture on a computer screen that is clicked to run a program is called
   a) a button   b) an icon
   c) a GUI   d) a menu.

2 A program is run by the
   a) RAM   b) ROM
   c) microprocessor   d) hard disk.

3 An ordinary computer keyboard is called
   a) a concept keyboard
   b) a keypad
   c) an ergonomic keyboard
   d) a QWERTY keyboard.

4 An inkjet printer
   a) can print carbon copies
   b) is the fastest type of printer
   c) can print in colour
   d) is suitable for printing many copies on a network.

5 To move an image from one place to another in a DTP document, the action needed is called
   a) drag and drop
   b) point and click
   c) copy and paste
   d) edit and copy.

Score .... /5

Q | Answer all parts of all questions.

1 What type of keyboard is suitable for each of these?

a) changing TV channels ....

b) entering what a customer bought in a restaurant at the checkout ....

c) entering a PIN at a bank machine ....

d) typing lots of text .... (4 marks)

2 Give two advantages of using flat screen monitors instead of cathode ray tubes.
.... (2 marks)

3 What type of printer is suitable for small-scale home use where colour is required?
.... (1 mark)

4 When an advertisement says that a computer has 'Intel Inside', what does this mean?
.... (2 marks)

5 What are the differences between ROM and RAM?
.... (2 marks)

Score .... /11

E **This is an exam-style question. Answer all parts of the question.**

Inderjit runs a small company that designs and prints CD and DVD covers. He wants to get himself a computer system that will help him and his assistants to do the design work and also look after all the other jobs that need doing in a business.
Inderjit goes to a computer supplier who tells him that he should get a PC with

- 256Mb of RAM
- a 17-inch flat screen monitor
- a good quality QWERTY keyboard
- a CD writer for copying big files

- a big hard disk
- a fast processor
- an optical mouse which does not pick up dirt.

He is also advised to buy a colour laser printer.

1 A 17 inch monitor is bigger than most people buy. Explain why Inderjit needs this.

.... (2 marks)

2 Describe three actions that Inderjit would need to use the mouse for when he is designing the CD covers.

.... (3 marks)

3 What will be stored in the RAM of his computer when it is running?

.... (3 marks)

4 How does the processor connect to the other parts of the computer?

.... (2 marks)

5 Inderjit takes the supplier's advice about the printer.
    a) What other types of printer might Inderjit have considered?

.... (2 marks)

    b) Why did the supplier recommend a colour laser printer?

.... (2 marks)

    c) What disadvantage might there be in choosing the colour laser printer?

.... (2 marks)

6 What will Inderjit store on the hard disk?

.... (3 marks)

7 Some of the items recommended by the supplier are peripherals. Which ones?

....

.... (4 marks)

8 State three other items of hardware that Inderjit might need.

.... (3 marks)

Score .... /26

TOTAL SCORE   /42

For more help on this topic see KS3 ICT Success Guide pages 8–9

SOFTWARE

M **Choose just one answer, a, b, c or d.**

1 A formula is most likely to be used in which type of software?
a) desktop publishing
b) Internet browser
c) spreadsheet
d) graphics software

2 The software that controls the computer hardware is called
a) an operating system
b) an application
c) a utility
d) control software.

3 The shape and design of the letters that are displayed in a word processor are called a
a) style   b) font
c) template   d) format.

4 A relational database organises data in
a) tables   b) forms
c) queries   d) relationships.

5 Which of these jobs is carried out by an operating system?
a) working out expenses
b) controlling traffic lights
c) storing a file on disk
d) writing a report

Score .... /5

Q **Answer all parts of all questions.**

1 a) What is an icon?

.... (2 marks)

b) What item of hardware is normally used to work with an icon?

.... (1 mark)

2 What is an application?

.... (2 marks)

3 Name any computer operating system.

.... (1 mark)

4 Which three of these jobs can be carried out by a computer application?

a) booking a hotel ....

b) printing a document ....

c) controlling a disk drive ....

d) finding space in memory for a program ....

e) working out payments to staff ....

f) controlling a plane .... (3 marks)

Score .... /9

12

This is an exam-style question. Answer all parts of the question.

Melissa is starting up her own business. She wants to run a scuba diving school in Australia. She first of all makes a multimedia presentation that she wants to run automatically in the local tourist office.

1 a) What is meant by multimedia?

.... (3 marks)

b) Why is multimedia a good way to promote a business?

.... (2 marks)

2 Melissa wants to make a large illustrated advertisement to go in the local papers as well. What software would be suitable for doing this? Give your reasons.

.... (3 marks)

3 a) Melissa is trying to work out how many pupils she needs to get in order to make enough money to pay all her bills. What type of software will help her most to do this?

.... (1 mark)

b) Explain how Melissa can use this software to show her bank manager very quickly how many pupils she hopes to get each month for the first year.

.... (3 marks)

4 Melissa organises all her records to do with the scuba diving school on a computer floppy disk. She intends to copy this onto her hard disk later. When she has finished, it looks like this:

a) How many directories (folders) has she made? ....

b) How many of these are sub directories? ....

c) How many files has she saved so far in the open folder? ....

d) What software did she use to set up the directories? ....

e) Give one advantage of organising these directories. ....

.... (5 marks)

5 State one use that Melissa might have for a database when running her business.

.... (2 marks)

Score .... /19

TOTAL SCORE   /33

For more help on this topic see KS3 ICT Success Guide pages 10–11

DATA AND INFORMATION

M | **Choose just one answer, a, b, c or d.**

1 The smallest amount of data that a computer can store is
   a) 1 byte
   b) 1 kilobyte
   c) 1 Megabyte
   d) 1 bit.

2 A stored set of data on a disk is called
   a) a file
   b) a record
   c) a program
   d) a table.

3 Which of these holds the least amount of data?
   a) a hard disk
   b) a CD
   c) a floppy disk
   d) a DVD

4 The operating system software that someone uses on a PC is normally loaded into memory from
   a) the hard disk
   b) a CD
   c) a memory stick
   d) a floppy disk.

5 What happens to the data in RAM when the computer is switched off?
   a) it is all copied onto the hard disk
   b) it disappears
   c) it is stored in ROM
   d) it stays in RAM

Score .... /5

Q | **Answer all parts of all questions.**

1 Many people store their work on flash drives.
  Where, on a computer, do flash drives need to be plugged in?

  .... (1 mark)

2 What type of device is used in a CD drive to write data onto a CDRW?

  .... (1 mark)

3 What is the difference between data and information?

  .... (2 marks)

4 A bit (binary digit) can have the value 0 or 1.
  Explain how this can be used to give the result of a decision.

  .... (2 marks)

5 Give three reasons why it is better to work on a hard disk rather than directly onto a floppy disk.

  ....

  .... (3 marks)

Score .... /9

E This is an exam-style question. Answer all parts of the question.

Kylie is buying a new computer to help her with her school work. She gets one that has a CD writer and she also buys a 64 Mb USB flash drive.

1 Describe three uses that Kylie might have for the CD writer.

....

.... (3 marks)

2 Kylie is working on a multimedia project at school. Explain why she uses her flash drive rather than a floppy disk to bring her work home.

.... (2 marks)

3 How else could Kylie bring her work home from the school's computers?

.... (2 marks)

4 Kylie has lots of graphics files stored on some old floppy disks. She wants to copy them onto her flash drive to take them to school to use in her multimedia project. How many disks can she copy onto her flash drive? How did you work that out?

.... (2 marks)

5 When Kylie tries to copy one of the old floppy disks, the computer cannot read it and displays an error message. She finds that the data on the disk has been corrupted although the disk looks in perfect condition. Give two reasons why this problem could have occurred?

.... (2 marks)

6 One day, Kylie goes to school and finds that the network server has crashed and everybody's data has been lost. Luckily, the technician is able to recover all the lost data. Explain how he has been able to do this.

....

.... (3 marks)

Score .... /14

TOTAL SCORE   /28

For more help on this topic see KS3 ICT Success Guide pages 12–13

SOURCES OF INFORMATION

M | Choose just one answer, a, b, c or d.

1 A website has the address camford.ac.uk. It most likely belongs to
a) a government body
b) a private company
c) a private individual
d) a university.

2 A website has the address camford.ac.uk. Its domain name suffix is
a) .ac.uk
b) .uk
c) camford
d) camford.ac

3 An argument is said to be biased if it is
a) wrong
b) balanced
c) one-sided
d) provocative.

4 Which of these is the best reason for being careful about believing what you see on websites?
a) most websites are biased
b) anyone can publish on the web
c) most websites are out of date
d) websites can be produced very cheaply

5 When you buy a book, the copyright of that book belongs to
a) you
b) the author
c) the publisher
d) the bookseller.

Score .... /5

Q | Answer all parts of all questions.

1 Give two reasons why illegal copying of music is more common than it used to be.
.... (2 marks)

2 What is plagiarism?
.... (2 marks)

3 a) State three ways that you could find out what is on television tonight.
.... (3 marks)

b) Give one advantage that each method has over the others.
.... (3 marks)

4 a) State three ways that you could find out about traffic conditions on the M25 at the present moment.
.... (3 marks)

b) Comment on which of these ways would be the most reliable and give a reason.
.... (2 marks)

Score .... /15

E **This is an exam-style question. Answer all parts of the question.**

Laura has an assignment to do. She has to investigate global warming. She has done some initial reading and has found that some scientists think that global warming is happening because of the excessive burning of fossil fuels. Other scientists think that the world's climate changes from time to time anyway and that it has nothing to do with the activities of mankind. Laura has to first collect a range of opinions.

1   List three sources of scientific information that will help Laura with her assignment.

....

....

.... (3 marks)

2   Which of these sources is likely to be the most reliable. Explain your reasoning.

.... (2 marks)

3   Which of these sources is most likely to be up-to-date? Explain why.

.... (2 marks)

4   Laura finds an article about global warming on a newsgroup called alt.globalwarming. Describe how far Laura can trust a site like this.

.... (2 marks)

5   Laura finds a website called
    http://yosemite.epa.gov/oar/globalwarming.nsf/content/climate.html
    This site has lots of information about global warming.
    What could she do to judge whether it is likely to be reliable?

....

.... (3 marks)

6   She finds out that 'epa' in the URL stands for Environmental Protection Agency and that it is put there by the US government. What does this tell her about the reliability of the site?

.... (2 marks)

7   Laura copies and pastes large sections of this website into her assignment and gives it in. What should she do to avoid being accused of plagiarism?

.... (2 marks)

Score .... /16

TOTAL SCORE   /36

For more help on this topic see KS3 ICT Success Guide pages 16–17

DATA AND FILES

M — Choose just one answer, a, b, c or d.

1 Which data type is suitable for storing a postcode?
   a) number   b) text
   c) alphabetic   d) memo

2 Which of these types of software is most suitable for creating and editing HTML code for a web page?
   a) text editor
   b) word processor
   c) desktop publishing software
   d) Internet browser

3 Which of these gives you an idea about what type of data is stored in a file?
   a) the file name   b) the file size
   c) the file extension d) the file attributes

4 A file on a disk is called fred.jpg. This file is likely to be
   a) a movie file   b) a word processed file
   c) a music file   d) an image file.

5 RTF stands for
   a) random type file   b) rich text format
   c) real text file   d) readable text format.

Score .... /5

Q — Answer all parts of all questions.

1 Explain why a file saved in word processor format will not display properly as a web page.

.... (3 marks)

2 When File-Open is selected from spreadsheet software, a list of all the existing spreadsheet files is shown. How does the software distinguish these from other files that are available?

.... (2 marks)

3 What is a boolean data type?

.... (1 mark)

4 a) How are dates stored in a computer system?

.... (1 mark)

   b) Explain one advantage of storing dates in this way.

.... (2 marks)

5 Why should a telephone number be stored as text instead of as a number?

.... (2 marks)

Score .... /11

E **This is an exam-style question. Answer all parts of the question.**

Wayne is a driving instructor. He is setting up a database to hold details about his pupils and his appointments. Somewhere on his computer hard disk, he already has a list of some of his pupils that he set up with a spreadsheet some time ago, but he cannot remember what he called it.

1 a) How can Wayne find all the spreadsheet files on his hard disk?

.... (2 marks)

   b) Explain how Wayne can make sure that he does not have so many problems finding files in the future?

.... (2 marks)

2 a) In the new database, Wayne needs to store details about when his appointments are. What data type is suitable for storing these details?

.... (1 mark)

   b) When a pupil has finished a lesson, Wayne looks up his database on his laptop and the system automatically suggests that the next lesson should be in one week and fills the date in. Explain how the system can generate the correct date.

.... (2 marks)

3 Wayne wants to get his computer to print out a reminder note to each pupil with the pupil's name and the date of the next appointment. How can he do this?

.... (2 marks)

4 Wayne wants a list of people who didn't turn up for their lessons so he makes a field to store this fact. What is the best choice of data type for this field?

.... (1 mark)

5 a) Wayne makes an advertisement to put in the local newspaper. He wants to e-mail it to the paper and the editorial staff at the paper ask him to send it as an RTF file. Why do they do this?

.... (2 marks)

   b) Later, Wayne loads his advertisement into his text editor to check that it is exactly as he wanted it. He sees text that looks like this:

{Wayne

\rquote s Driving School

\par }\pard\plain \qc \li0\ri0\widctlpar\aspalpha\aspnum\faauto\adjustright\rin0\lin0\itap0

\fs24\lang2057\langfe1033\cgrid\langnp2057\langfenp1033 {\b

\par }\pard \ql \li0\ri0\widctlpar\aspalpha\aspnum\faauto\adjustright\rin0\lin0\itap0 {More people pass every year with Wayne\rquote s Driving School than with anyone else.

\par }}

Explain what has happened.

.... (3 marks)

Score .... /15

TOTAL SCORE /31

For more help on this topic see KS3 ICT Success Guide pages 18–19

GRAPHICS AND SOUND

M — Choose just one answer, a, b, c or d.

1 Approximately how much storage will be required to hold a full screen bitmapped image?
a) 1 byte
b) 1 Kilobyte
c) 1 Megabyte
d) 1 Gigabyte

2 Drawing tools in a word processor produce
a) bitmapped graphics
b) raster graphics
c) vector graphics
d) compressed graphics.

3 An MP3 file is used for storing
a) images
b) music
c) text
d) program instructions.

4 Bitmapped images are made up from lots of
a) pixels
b) lines
c) numbers
d) instructions.

5 A vector graphic software package would be suitable for
a) editing a scanned photograph
b) painting a picture
c) drawing a diagram for an experiment
d) compressing an image file.

Score .... /5

Q — Answer all parts of all questions.

1 a) What is analogue data?

.... (2 marks)

b) What is digital data?

.... (2 marks)

2 Sound is an analogue form of energy but music CDs are a digital medium. Explain how this can happen.

....
.... (3 marks)

3 a) Why are images often compressed before being used on a website?

....
.... (3 marks)

b) State one type of image compression format.

.... (1 mark)

c) State one disadvantage that can result from image compression.

.... (1 mark)

Score .... /12

This is an exam-style question. Answer all parts of the question.

Alice is making a collection of digital photos of all her friends. She wants them for her own collection and also to send them by e-mail to those who live a long way away. She goes out to buy a digital camera. The shop has 2 megapixel and 6 megapixel cameras for sale.

1 a) Explain what difference there will be in the photos produced by these two types of camera.

.... (2 marks)

b) The 2 megapixel camera is much cheaper. Alice is told that it will be quite good as long as she does not want to make big enlargements. Why is the size of enlargement a factor to consider?

.... (3 marks)

c) Alice buys the 2 megapixel camera and also an extra memory card for the camera. She is told that it can hold between 50 and 200 photos depending on how the camera is set up. What setting on the camera will affect how many pictures will fit on the card?

.... (1 mark)

d) Alice soon builds up a big collection of photos which she downloads onto her PC. She wants to make sure that the photos are backed up in case she ever has a problem with her PC. What would be a suitable storage medium to hold the pictures? Explain your answer.

.... (3 marks)

2 Alice is about to send some pictures to her friends as e-mail attachments. She only has a slow modem Internet connection. What should she do to make sure that she is not online for too long? Explain your answer.

.... (2 marks)

3 Alice wants to print out some of her best photos to go into frames. The results don't look as good as they do on the screen. Explain possible reasons for this.

.... (2 marks)

Score .... /13

TOTAL SCORE   /30

For more help on this topic see KS3 ICT Success Guide pages 20–21

DATABASES

M Choose just one answer, a, b, c or d.

1 A PIN is a
   a) paying-in number
   b) personal identification name
   c) personal identification number
   d) paying-in note.

2 Which of these services makes use of a database of websites?
   a) a chat room   b) a search engine
   c) an e-mail program d) a book-ordering system

3 What is a mobile phone base station?
   a) the headquarters where the bills are produced
   b) the exchange where calls are connected to land lines
   c) the tower and equipment that communicates with handsets
   d) the office where the computers that control the calls are located

4 A database is
   a) hardware
   b) software
   c) a store of data
   d) a query for locating data.

5 Which of these is a likely use of a database in a school?
   a) sending letters home to parents about a school concert
   b) making signs to identify different rooms
   c) controlling the burglar alarm system
   d) locating the telephone number of a parent whose child is ill

Score .... /5

Q Answer all parts of all questions.

1 Describe two reasons why a bank's database has to be looked up when someone makes a withdrawal at a cash machine.

.... (2 marks)

2 a) What is the database used by a supermarket when an item is scanned at the checkout?

.... (1 mark)

b) State two items of data that are looked up in that database when the item is scanned.

.... (2 marks)

3 Give three advantages that databases have over information stored on paper.

.... (3 marks)

22

Q **Continued**

4 The DVLA (Driver and Vehicle Licensing Agency) keeps a database of all UK–registered vehicles and drivers. Give three occasions when the police might need to look details up in this database.

.... (3 marks)

Score .... /11

E **This is an exam-style question. Answer all parts of the question.**

Charlie lives in the UK and is going on holiday abroad. He needs to look up suitable holidays and make all the necessary arrangements. He first of all goes to a travel agent to choose his holiday.

1 What databases might the travel agent have to consult?

....

.... (3 marks)

2 Charlie wants to use his mobile phone when he goes abroad. He needs to get the phone company to 'unlock' the systems of foreign phone providers and provide his details to them. Why will the foreign phone providers need access to Charlie's database records?

.... (2 marks)

3 a) If Charlie has an accident when on holiday, it would help the foreign doctors if they had online access to a database in the UK. How could that help them?

.... (2 marks)

   b) So that Charlie would get the best treatment, what are the most important considerations in maintaining the UK database that the doctors look at?

.... (2 marks)

4 Charlie needs to draw some money when on holiday. The foreign banks have a connection to the UK bank databases. How can this help Charlie?

.... (2 marks)

Score .... /11

TOTAL SCORE /27

For more help on this topic see KS3 ICT Success Guide pages 22–23

DATA CAPTURE FORMS

M Choose just one answer, a, b, c or d.

1 Data capture is
   a) copying data from one computer to another
   b) sending data over the Internet
   c) gathering data from the real world in a way suitable for computer processing
   d) checking that data is accurate.

2 Which of these processes is most likely to produce structured data?
   a) interviewing people
   b) holding a meeting
   c) giving out a questionnaire
   d) observing people at work

3 A check box on a computer screen is a good way to collect
   a) yes/no data   b) a long comment
   c) someone's age   d) someone's surname.

4 Why are character boxes helpful on forms?
   a) they remind the user how to enter the data
   b) they make sure that the data is always accurate
   c) they restrict how much can be written
   d) they help the user to fill in the form more completely

5 A drop-down box on a computer form is most suitable for
   a) entering a lot of text
   b) choosing one item from a limited range of options
   c) confirming that the data is all correct
   d) editing existing text.

Score .... /5

Q Answer all parts of all questions.

1 What is the purpose of a command button on a computer screen form?

.... (1 mark)

2 Give three rules for making a paper form easy to use.

.... (3 marks)

3 Give three reasons why market researchers might want to use questionnaires instead of interviewing people when investigating what people think of a product.

.... (3 marks)

4 Give two ways that a computer screen form can be arranged to reduce the possibility of errors being entered.

.... (2 marks)

Score .... /9

E This is an exam-style question. Answer all parts of the question.

Daisy runs a garden centre. She sells plants by post. When a customer wants to order some plants, there is a form to fill in that has to be sent to Daisy.

1 Give three reasons why this form is badly designed.

.... (3 marks)

2 Make three suggestions about how this form could be improved.

.... (3 marks)

3 Screen forms contain controls to make it easier to work with the computer. Match each of the controls labelled A–E with a suitable use in Daisy's Garden Centre, listed below.

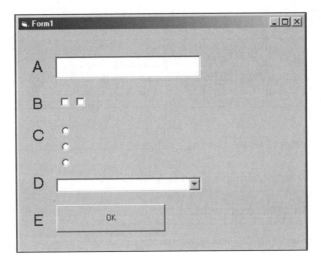

(i) Entering a customer's name
(ii) Submitting a completed order
(iii) Choosing from a list of available plant types
(iv) Choosing from different methods of payment
(v) Choosing whether to send by post or to be collected

.... (5 marks)

Score .... /11

TOTAL SCORE /25

For more help on this topic see KS3 ICT Success Guide pages 24–25

STRUCTURING DATA

M Choose just one answer, a, b, c or d.

1 Which of these would make a suitable key field in a student data table?
a) surname   b) date of birth
c) student number   d) address

2 In a relational database, the data is stored in
a) tables   b) reports
c) forms   d) queries.

3 In a database of computers for sale, all the data about one particular computer would make up
a) a field   b) a record
c) a table   d) a file.

4 In a student database, the surname of one pupil is
a) a field   b) a record
c) a table   d) a file.

5 A database stores data about mobile phone contracts. A customer is
a) a field   b) a file
c) a table   d) an entity.

Score .... /5

Q Answer all parts of all questions.

Here is part of a database.

customer_ref	surname	forename	title	address1	address2	address3	post_code	telephone
0	Kelly	John	Mr	4 Long Road	Smithtown	Lancs	LL773TT	67666776
1	Jackson	Chris	Dr	12 George Street	Chelmsford	Essex	CM1 3EE	67867886
2	Guy	Gregory	Mr	14 Third Street	Lincoln	Lincs	LN5 6TT	34578767
3	Smith	Jack	Mr	10 High Street	Smithtown	Lancs	SM7 8UY	67867868
4	Green	Mary	Mrs	100 Pershore Road	Evesham	Worcs	WR99 8UU	56776556
5	Black	Harry	Rev	The Vicarage	Church Road	Churchill	CH7 6TT	46756765

1 a) How many records are there? .... (1 mark)

b) How many fields are there? .... (1 mark)

c) Which field is a suitable key field? .... (1 mark)

d) Which field could have a numeric data type? .... (1 mark)

e) Which field needs a field size maximum of 3 bytes? .... (1 mark)

2 a) What is a simple one-table database called? .... (1 mark)

b) Give one situation where such a simple database would be suitable.

.... (1 mark)

3 Give two possible data types that could be used to store the price of an item in a shop.

.... (2 marks)

Score .... /9

E **This is an exam-style question. Answer all parts of the question.**

A concert-booking agency takes bookings from members of the public. It deals with over 20 venues, each of which holds many concerts each year. It uses a database to handle the bookings and print tickets.

1 What entities are needed in this situation?

....

....

.... (3 marks)

2 What information would be needed from the customer in order to make a booking?

....

....

.... (3 marks)

3 When the ticket is printed, what items will be printed from data

a) looked up in the database ....

....

b) obtained from other sources? ....

.... (3 marks)

4 The data stored about a concert includes its date, the artist(s) (up to 30 letters) and the venue (up to 20 letters).
How much storage space would be needed to hold 100 concert records?

....

....

.... (3 marks)

Score .... /12

TOTAL SCORE /26

VALIDATION AND VERIFICATION

M Choose just one answer, a, b, c or d.

1 A computer operator types in Amanda's name as Aman8a by mistake. This error can be highlighted by a
a) check digit validation
b) type check
c) range check
d) length check.

2 Validation is designed to trap errors during
a) data processing   b) data transmission
c) data input   d) data storage.

3 Some data entry systems require data to be input twice. This is to ensure that the data is
a) correct   b) reasonable
c) reliable   d) not corrupted.

4 A shop sells nothing over £10. When entering prices into its database, it is impossible to enter a price of £11. This is because the software has used a
a) length check   b) check digit
c) type check   d) range check.

5 When numeric data is to be transmitted, it is sometimes all added up before being sent. The result is sent with the data. This result is called a
a) checksum   b) parity check
c) check digit   d) key.

Score .... /5

Q Answer all parts of all questions.

Huw Thomas applies for a job as a sales executive. He has eight GCSEs, two A levels, two years' experience in a similar job and he is 25 years old.

Surname:	Thomas
Forename:	Huww
Date of birth:	22/12/701
Number of GCSE passes:	10
Number of A levels:	27
Years experience (enter a number):	TWO

Part of his application form is shown here.

1 a) List the factual mistakes on this form.

.... (2 marks)

b) State two mistakes that could be sensibly spotted by the data entry software. For each mistake, state the type of check that could detect it.

....

.... (4 marks)

2 What steps are taken during double entry verification?

.... (3 marks)

3 What type of validation is used when reading bar codes of items that are being scanned?

.... (1 mark)

4 Describe one drawback to using double entry verification.

.... (2 marks)

Score .... /12

E   **This is an exam-style question. Answer all parts of the question.**

Nadia wants to open a web-based e-mail account. She has to fill in an on-screen form to give the mailing company her details.

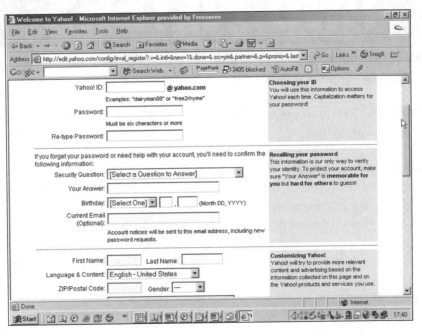

1   The information will not be processed if the user's ID or password are omitted.

a)   What is the reason for this?

.... (2 marks)

b)   What type of validation prevents this?

.... (1 mark)

c)   What feature on the form prevents the user from entering a spelling mistake in the month field?

.... (1 mark)

d)   Why is the gender field a drop-down box?

.... (2 marks)

2   Some people try to disguise their age when taking out e-mail or chat room accounts. What can the software do to avoid situations like this?

.... (2 marks)

3   The form asks for a zip code for an American address. Explain how the validation rules would change if the user chose UK instead of US.

.... (2 marks)

Score .... /10

TOTAL SCORE   /27

For more help on this topic see KS3 ICT Success Guide pages 28–29

QUERIES, INDEXES AND FILTERS

M Choose just one answer, a, b, c or d.

1 Which of these is a way to search a database?
a) a query
b) a form
c) a report
d) a macro

2 A database search can be speeded up by making
a) a macro
b) a primary key
c) an index
d) a validation rule.

3 QBE is a way of making a query
a) by writing program code
b) by writing a statement
c) by writing a macro
d) by filling in a grid.

4 To make a query, you have to specify
a) the table, the field and the condition
b) the table, the record and the field
c) the record, the field and the condition
d) the record, the table and the condition.

5 A way to show only a selected part of a spreadsheet is to use a
a) sort
b) window
c) filter
d) column format.

Score .... /5

Q Answer all parts of all questions.

1 List three things that a database query can do.

.... (3 marks)

2 A query is written that says:

SELECT patient_number, patient_name, illness FROM patients WHERE illness="diabetes"

a) What is the name of the table being queried?

.... (1 mark)

b) How many fields are being asked for?

.... (1 mark)

c) What condition is being used in this query?

.... (1 mark)

3 a) What is a database report?

.... (1 mark)

b) How can you make a report only look at certain records?

.... (1 mark)

Score .... /8

E **This is an exam-style question. Answer all parts of the question.**

Greg is a biologist. He works with flies. He is working out the relationship between the time of year when their eggs hatch, the length of their pupation and their final body length. Here is a part of his records which he has entered into a spreadsheet.

Fly_number	Month_hatched	Length_of_pupation	Adult_length
1	Jan	45	9
2	Jan	43	7
3	Jan	47	8
4	Jan	40	6
5	Jan	39	7
6	Jan	42	8
7	Jan	43	9
8	Jul	24	11
9	Jul	25	13
10	Jul	23	14
11	Jul	26	12
12	Jul	22	13
13	Jul	24	11
14	Jul	21	10
15	Jul	22	13

1 a) How would Greg get the spreadsheet software to display only the details of flies that were longer than 10 mm?

.... (3 marks)

b) Greg now wants to see details of all the flies that were hatched in January, with pupation lengths of less than 40 days. What must he now do?

.... (4 marks)

2 As Greg gets more results, he decides to export his spreadsheet data into a relational database.
a) What does export mean in this case?

.... (2 marks)

b) The data is now in a data table called 'flies'. Explain how Greg can set up a query to get the same results as he did in question 1(b).

....

.... (4 marks)

c) Write a statement that achieves the same result. (Hint: SQL)

....

.... (4 marks)

Score .... /17

TOTAL SCORE /30

For more help on this topic see KS3 ICT Success Guide pages 30–31

REPORTS

M Choose just one answer, a, b, c or d.

1 Which of these is a job that can be done with a database report?
a) store a set of data
b) set out data on a screen for data entry
c) group data
d) validate data

2 A database report can be based on a
a) query   b) form
c) macro   d) text box.

3 A database report is an example of
a) a user interface   b) hard copy
c) data input   d) data storage.

4 Which of these tasks cannot be done by a query wizard?
a) create totals in a query
b) enter data into a table
c) link two tables
d) select criteria

5 When designing a heading to go on a report, the best object to use is a
a) combo box
b) command button
c) data grid
d) label.

Score .... /5

Q Answer all parts of all questions.

1 a) Explain how a wizard can help to produce a report in a database.

.... (2 marks)

b) Give two examples of information that you have to give to a report wizard.

.... (2 marks)

2 a) A teacher has a database of students. One table contains their exam results. Give two examples where a report of this database could be useful.

.... (2 marks)

b) The student database also contains a table of which classes the students belong to. Explain how a report can be set up to include this information as well as the results.

.... (3 marks)

3 How can a table wizard help someone to get working on entering data as quickly as possible?

.... (2 marks)

Score .... /11

E **This is an exam-style question. Answer all parts of the question.**

Gus is a travel agent who makes hotel bookings for customers. He has a database of the hotels that he uses. He wants to print out a report that summarises all the hotels that he deals with in each area. The report must look like this:

1 a) How many fields are needed for the report?

.... (1 mark)

b) How many records are showing in this part of the report?

.... (1 mark)

c) This report was created partly by using a wizard. The wizard asked Gus 'Do you want to add any grouping levels?'

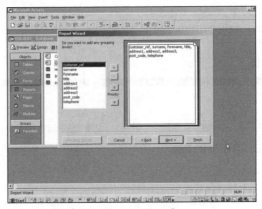

What did Gus click on to answer that question?

.... (1 mark)

d) Gus was then asked 'What sort order do you want?' What did he choose?

.... (1 mark)

e) Finally, Gus was asked what title he wanted for the report. What did he reply?

.... (1 mark)

2 Explain why people often want reports from a database.

.... (2 marks)

Score .... /7

TOTAL SCORE /23

For more help on this topic see KS3 ICT Success Guide pages 32–33

SEARCH ENGINES

M Choose just one answer, a, b, c or d.

1 Which of these methods will help a website to get noticed by a search engine?
   a) include lots of graphics
   b) the use of frames
   c) include meta-tags
   d) include applets

2 When using a search engine, you type your question into a box. What you type is called
   a) a query
   b) a search string
   c) a search parameter
   d) a search function.

3 Which of these linking words increases the number of hits that a search engine turns up?
   a) AND   b) OR
   c) NOT   d) NOR

4 Which of these words restricts the number of matching sites that a search engine will turn up?
   a) AND   b) OR
   c) NOT   d) NOR

5 Which of these search engine enquiries will probably find the fewest pages?
   a) motor racing
   b) Grand Prix 2004
   c) "Track times in the British Grand Prix 2004"
   d) Track times in the British Grand Prix 2004

Score .... /5

Q Answer all parts of all questions.

1 Give three ways in which a web designer can make sure that search engines direct people to his or her site as soon as possible.

   .... (3 marks)

2 Jack is having trouble with his computer. It keeps producing annoying pop-up messages whenever he is on the Internet. He goes to a search engine and types in *computer problems*.

   a) Why is this unlikely to be of much help to him?

   .... (3 marks)

   b) Give some advice on how Jack can use the Internet to find out what the problem is and how to cure it.

   .... (3 marks)

3 Describe two ways in which search engines build up their databases of websites.

   .... (3 marks)

4 What is the effect of putting speech marks around a search engine enquiry?

   .... (1 mark)

Score .... /13

E **This is an exam-style question. Answer all parts of the question.**

Mario is opening a restaurant in Chiswick, London. He wants to get noticed straightaway so he has set up a website. After two weeks, his hit counter tells him that very few people have visited the website.

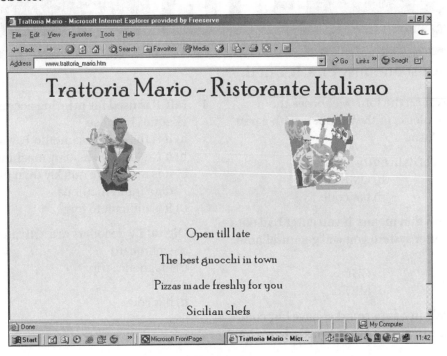

1   Suggest some meta-tags that will encourage local people to visit his website.

.... (3 marks)

2   a) How can Mario make sure that the search engines have information about his website?

.... (1 mark)

   b) Suggest another way that Mario can increase the likelihood of people visiting his website.

.... (1 mark)

3   Jo lives in West London and wants to find an Italian restaurant in Chiswick. She goes to a search engine and types in *Italian restaurant*. She gets over 4 million 'hits'. She then tries it with speech marks: *"Italian restaurant"* and gets 797,000 hits.
   a) Explain why there are fewer hits the second time.

.... (2 marks)

   b) 797,000 websites are still too many to look at, so Jo needs to narrow her search down. How can she do this?

.... (2 marks)

   c) The next week, Jo wants to eat out again, but this time she wants to go to either a Thai or a Chinese restaurant. How can she best get a shortlist of options?

.... (2 marks)

Score .... /11

TOTAL SCORE   /29

For more help on this topic see KS3 ICT Success Guide pages 34–35

AUTOMATIC DATA ENTRY

M Choose just one answer, a, b, c or d.

1 When a player on the lottery chooses the numbers, he blocks in the numbers with a pen on a special form.

This method of data entry is called
a) OCR b) OMR
c) MICR d) bar code.

2 An expression that means 'if you enter bad data into a computer system you will get unreliable results' is
a) WIMP b) GUI
c) GIGO d) MICR.

3 Goods for sale in a supermarket have bar codes on them. One item that is not encoded on a bar code is
a) the price
b) the product identity
c) the country of origin
d) the manufacturer's identity.

4 MICR is used for printing account details on cheques because
a) it is the cheapest method available
b) it can only be read by machine
c) it is read more quickly than other automatic data input methods
d) it is difficult to forge.

5 Digital TV decoders are activated by a
a) smart card
b) magnetic strip
c) PIN
d) bar code.

Score .... /5

Q Answer all parts of all questions.

1 Give three situations where smart cards are used.

.... (3 marks)

2 a) What is a turnaround document?

.... (3 marks)

b) Give one situation where a turnaround document might be useful.

.... (1 mark)

3 Explain why automatic data entry is preferred to human data entry.

.... (3 marks)

4 Give three examples of where magnetic strips are used to store data.

.... (3 marks)

Score .... /13

Letts

KS3

SUCCESS

QUESTIONS & ANSWERS

ICT

Sean O'Byrne

ANSWER BOOK

WHAT IS ICT?

Section M
1. a
2. d
3. c
4. a
5. c

Section Q
1. a) dimensions of walls/ceilings, how much paint covers what area, price of paint, how many rooms. **Any 2**
   b) cost of painting one room, total cost, an area calculated, how much paint needed. **Any 2**
   c) calculate total cost, calculate how much paint needed, calculate wall/ceiling areas. **Any 2**
2. Examples: microwave oven, washing machine, video, CD player, DVD player, camera, dishwasher, phone, computer, PDA. **Any 3**
3. Much of the production is carried out by computer controlled machines, this gives greater accuracy
4. They run programs, these can give them different sets of instructions

Section E
1. Date of concert, price she is willing to pay, location of seat, location of venue. **Any 2**
2. Seats available, costs, locations. **Any 2**
3. Name, address, credit card details, choice of tickets, how many tickets. **Any 3**
4. Printing the tickets, recording the sale of the tickets, printing the address. **Any 2**
5. a) CDs, download from the Internet
   b) easy to copy, high quality, does not lose quality when copied. **Any 2**
   c) illegal copying / copyright infringement, reduces sales, therefore less incentive to produce new music
6. DVDs of films, digital television, digital radio, personal music players, special effects in films, computer games, Internet chat. **Any 4**
7. Mobile phone is almost certainly digital, taxi firm may use computer booking system, taxi may use GPS to find the way. **Any 2**

ICT IN SOCIETY

Section M
1. d
2. c
3. b
4. c
5. a

Section Q
1. clearer signal, more users can share one channel, more reliable. **Any 2**
2. too complicated, too expensive, difficulty in linking up so many doctors/hospitals/health centres. **Any 2**
3. any form of record keeping, presentations, making resources, communicating with colleagues, researching for lessons. **Any 3**
4. better quality, more reliable, cheaper, more users can share channels. **Any 2**
5. patient records, drug records, look up treatments/drugs on the Internet, communicate with hospital. **Any 2**

Section E
1. saves office space, can use smaller premises
2. less travel, can work when he likes, more comfortable. **Any 2**
3. loneliness, miss out on developments at work, more distractions
4. modem or router, ISP connection, browser software, e-mail software. **Any 3**
5. cash machines, cash back in the supermarket, automatic bill payments, credit transfers, credit cards, direct debits. **Any 3**
6. hacking, someone might access his account, Trojan horse, passwords might be captured from his computer. **Any 2**
7. fewer mistakes made, fewer staff need to be employed, new services become possible, communication with customers is better. **Any 3**

HARDWARE

Section M
1. b
2. c
3. d
4. c
5. a

Section Q
1. a) remote control
   b) concept keyboard
   c) keypad
   d) QWERTY (ordinary) keyboard
2. clearer, take less space, take less current, do not generate as much heat. **Any 2**
3. inkjet
4. the processor is made by the Intel corporation

5. ROM is non-volatile / keeps its contents when power is off; RAM is volatile / loses its contents when power is off; more RAM than ROM; ROM stores permanently required routines; RAM stores user's programs / data. **Any 2**

Section E
1. he is doing graphics work, this requires a bigger / easier to view screen
2. selecting images, selecting text, dragging objects, dragging out frames, resizing objects
3. operating system, the application software such as DTP, the data files he is working on / text / images
4. buses, example such as control / data / address, cables. **Any 2**
5. a) dot matrix, inkjet
   b) better quality, more suitable for bigger print runs
   c) expensive to buy, expensive to run
6. operating system, all the applications he needs, e.g. DTP, word processor, graphics software, the work files. **Any 3**
7. monitor, keyboard, mouse, printer
8. digital camera, scanner, modem, router, network card. **Any 3**

SOFTWARE

Section M
1. c
2. a
3. b
4. a
5. b

Section Q
1. a) a picture, that represents a program (or other resource) on a computer system
   b) mouse
2. software, that is used to solve a real problem for a person
3. Examples: Windows, Linux, Unix, Mac OS. **Any 1**
4. a, e, f

Section E
1. a) a presentation that includes some of the following: text, graphics, movies, sound. **Any 3**
   b) more memorable/has more impact, can be quite cheap to set up, can show many different aspects of the business. **Any 2**
2. desktop publishing, because it allows designs to be made, text to be inserted, graphics to be inserted. **Any 3**
3. a) spreadsheet
   b) enter the figures, enter the months, highlight all this data, plot a chart, use the chart wizard. **Any 3**
4. a) 10
   b) 9
   c) 3
   d) operating system / Windows / Windows Explorer
   e) better organisation, easier to copy related files in one go
5. storing details, of pupils, of equipment. **Any 2**

DATA AND INFORMATION

Section M
1. d
2. a
3. c
4. a
5. b

Section Q
1. USB port
2. laser
3. data is just facts, information is data plus meaning
4. 1 means yes, 0 means no
5. floppy disks don't hold much data, they are slow, they are easily damaged

Section E
1. copying music, playing music, storing big files, making backups, running multimedia presentations such as an encyclopaedia, installing software. **Any 3**
2. multimedia files tend to be big, not enough room on a floppy disk
3. copy it onto a CD, e-mail it to herself
4. $64/1.44 = 44$ disks
5. magnetic fields, heat, dirt. **Any 2**
6. there was a backup, stored on tape, data copied back from the tape

SOURCES OF INFORMATION

Section M
1. d
2. a
3. c
4. b
5. b

Section Q
1. CD burners are cheap, no reduction in quality when digital music copied
2. copying someone else's work, and pretending that it is your own
3. a) TV announcements, paper/magazine listings, Internet, specialist magazine, ask someone. **Any 3**
   b) various answers are possible, but ideas are: TV announcements – might remind you about something that you hadn't noticed / up-to-date; paper – can read it anywhere – can compare the main channels; specialist magazine – more likely to see little-known programmes of special interest; ask someone – may have the same interests as you and have heard about programme. **Any 3 reasonable reasons**
4. a) CEEFAX, Internet site such as the AA, television,
   b) Internet – most likely to be up-to-date

Section E
1. journals, books, Internet sources, TV programmes, multimedia encyclopaedias. **Any 3**
2. arguments such as: books – probably edited/checked for accuracy; website – university source – probably up-to-date thinking. **1 for source – 1 for reason**
3. website – can be updated and published straightaway / less cost to update. **1 for source – 1 for reason**
4. need to be very sceptical. 'alt' signifies 'alternative' discussion group – could get absolutely anyone giving opinions here
5. examine the domain name, visit the site and see who has put it there, look for reasonable links on the site, judge quality by language used / presentation. **Any 3**
6. US government site, probably reliable, puts government point of view
7. give references, set out copied sections in quotes so it is obvious that they are quotes

DATA AND FILES

Section M
1. b
2. a
3. c
4. d
5. b

Section Q
1. word processed files store formatting codes, these are not understood by web browsers, the display will show the codes – not the intended format
2. the extension, indicates the file type
3. yes/no data
4. a) as numbers
   b) can calculate the difference between dates, by subtracting the numbers
5. telephone numbers have leading zeros, and spaces/dashes, these cannot be stored as numbers. **Any 2**

Section E
1. a) do a search, for all files with xls (spreadsheet) extension
   b) keep all related files in one folder, no need to search whole disk
2. a) data or date/time
   b) system holds the current date, can add on the right number of days
3. either – generate a report from the database or use mail merge, get data from the data table
4. boolean (yes/no)
5. a) the correct format is received, does not matter what software was used to set it up – compatible with most word processors.
   b) RTF contains embedded codes, to control display, text editor cannot use them, so displays the codes instead. **Any 3**

GRAPHICS AND SOUND

Section M
1. c
2. c
3. b
4. a
5. c

Section Q
1. a) data that can take any value, between the lowest and highest possible
   b) data that can take one of two values, on or off (yes/no, or 0 or 1)
2. sound is sampled, at intervals, values such as loudness and sound quality stored, as numbers. **Any 3**
3. a) images make big files, they take a long time to download, compression makes them smaller, reduces download times. **Any 3**
   b) jpeg, gif. **Any 1**
   c) detail can be lost

Section E
1. a) 6 megapixel camera will have higher resolution, therefore clearer pictures
   b) enlargement increases pixel size, this makes the dots more visible, so picture is not as clear as it should be
   c) resolution / quality
   d) CD, pictures are large files, CD has large capacity, CD is portable. **Any 3**
2. compress the files, so that they download faster
3. printer has lower resolution than the screen, paper quality poor

DATABASES

Section M
1. c
2. b
3. c
4. c
5. d

Section Q
1. check identity, check password, check balance, adjust balance. **Any 2**
2. a) stock database
   b) identity / name of item, price of item
3. quicker to search, take less space, easier to update, can be backed up, easy to be accessed by many users. **Any 3**
4. investigating stolen vehicles, investigating a crime where a vehicle was used, sending fines to motorists who are caught speeding

Section E
1. holidays, hotels, airlines, customer details. **Any 3**
2. to identify his phone, so that it can be located and transmitted to, for billing purposes. **Any 2**
3. a) access to medical records, would help in deciding the right treatment, useful to know about allergies/medical problems. **Any 2**
   b) up-to-date, accurate
4. balance checked immediately, identity checked, can clear for cash withdrawal immediately, because online. **Any 2**

DATA CAPTURE FORMS

Section M
1. c
2. c
3. a
4. c
5. b

Section Q
1. to be clicked on to make something happen
2. have a heading, use prompts, restrict the possible answers, use tick boxes or other quick methods where possible. **Any 3**
3. can reach more people, answers are structured, answers are restricted
4. drop-down boxes, check boxes, validate entries. **Any 2**

Section E
1. no prompts, no spaces set out for data entry, no format provided for name and address, no indication of how date is to be entered, no help with how to enter orders. **Any 3**
2. character boxes for name and address, formatted box for date, fields set out for order such as ref no, quantity and description, contact details for the garden centre. **Any 3**
3. i) A
   ii) E
   iii) D
   iv) C
   v) B

STRUCTURING DATA

Section M
1. c
2. a
3. b
4. a
5. d

Section Q
1. a) 6
   b) 9
   c) customer_ref
   d) customer_ref (only)
   e) title
2. a) a flat file database
   b) example: address book, inventory (any example where there is just one entity to store data about)
3. currency, number

Section E
1. venue, customer, concert, ticket. **Any 3**
2. name, address, concert date, venue, seat price/type, alternatives. **Any 3**
3. a) name of customer, concert date, venue, seat price, seat number
   b) booking date, agency name / details. **Any 3**
4. 5800 bytes
   58 bytes per record (8 bytes for date, 1 byte each per letter)
   100 records is 100*58

VALIDATION & VERIFICATION

Section M
1 b
2 c
3 a
4 d
5 a

Section Q
1 a) forename mis-spelt, year of birth impossible, number of GCSEs wrong, number of A levels wrong and probably impossible, years' experience non-numeric. **Any 2**
   b) date of birth – range check
      number of A levels – range check
      years' experience – type check
      1 mark each for field identified, plus 1 mark each for correct check
2 first person types data in, second person types same data in, software compares the two versions, discrepancies are highlighted, corrections made from source document. **Any 3**
3 check digit
4 work has to be done twice, so more expensive / takes longer

Section E
1 a) Without the ID, there can be no meaningful e-mail account. Without the password, there will be no security.
   b) presence check
   c) selection made from drop-down box
   d) only two values possible, prevents most mistakes
2 it can only validate impossible dates such as in the future or too long ago, apart from this, it can do nothing
3 picture / format code would change, to suit UK postcodes instead of US zip codes

QUERIES, INDEXES AND FILTERS

Section M
1 a
2 c
3 d
4 a
5 c

Section Q
1 can combine data from more than one table, can select on several fields, can extract records that match certain criteria
2 a) patients
   b) 3
   c) patients who have diabetes
3 a) printed output
   b) base it on a query

Section E
1 a) set a filter, on the length column, set to >10
   b) turn off the first filter, set filter on month_hatched, =Jan, set filter on length_of_pupation, <40
2 a) copy data, and convert it into a form suitable for different software
   b) enter the field names, into a QBE grid, set the criteria for month_hatched to be Jan, set the criteria for length_of_pupation to <40
   c) SELECT Fly_number, Month_hatched, length_of_pupation FROM flies, WHERE Month_hatched="JAN" AND length_of_pupation<40
      4 marks: 1 for the SELECT statement, 1 for the FROM statement, 1 for the WHERE statement, 1 for the AND statement

REPORTS

Section M
1 c
2 a
3 b
4 b
5 d

Section Q
1 a) it asks questions about the report, then creates it automatically
   b) name of table/query, fields wanted, grouping wanted, whether totals/averages wanted. **Any 2**
2 a) examples: list of pupils in order of marks, report to parents
   b) create a query, this includes fields from both tables, base report on the query
3 it creates the table, can choose from examples, can create a form at the same time for data entry

Section E
1 a) 4
   b) 9
   c) address3
   d) name
   e) Hotel report
2 to have hard copy, to take away, to read when not at the computer. **Any 2**

SEARCH ENGINES

Section M
1 c
2 b
3 b
4 a
5 c

Section Q
1 use meta-tags, inform the search engine website, include plenty of links
2 a) this is likely to be a very common topic on websites, so it will return a huge number of hits, very unlikely that his specific problem will be turned up
   b) the idea here is to be as specific as possible; use a search engine and enter "browser pop up", enter the content of the message, enter "browser security" – the use of quote marks may help to narrow it down
3 search for words within the web pages, search for meta-tags, search for titles/headings, follow links. **Any 3**
4 it requires a literal match

Section E
1 examples: Chiswick, London, restaurant, Italian, pizza, gnocchi. **Any 3**
2 a) inform the search engine website
   b) post links on local trade websites
3 a) Italian restaurant finds any mention of either word, speech marks require an exact match – so fewer exact matches
   b) add the word "Chiswick", keep Italian Restaurant in quotes, use the word AND between each of these words. **Any 2**
   c) include the words Thai and Chinese, link with OR, include Chiswick, link Chiswick with the other words with AND. **Any 2**

AUTOMATIC DATA ENTRY

Section M
1 b
2 c
3 a
4 d
5 a

Section Q
1 satellite TV boxes, cash cards, credit / debit cards, ID cards, SIM cards. **Any 3**
2 a) a document that is produced by a computer, then further information is added, then the new information is read by machine
   b) examples: forms for recording gas/electricity meter readings, patient data in hospital, class registers
3 automatic data entry is faster than human, more accurate, cheaper than employing a human
4 examples: credit / debit cards (older ones), travel tickets, car park tickets, hotel room keys. **Any 3**

Section E
1 a) bar code might be dirty / creased, therefore not all read correctly, check digit incorrect, signals an error condition. **Any 3**
   b) code is also printed in human readable form, can key in the code
2 a) magnetic strip, smart card
   b) card reader / scanner
3 a) restricts access to employees, so more likely to have space
   b) at least the company identity, possibly also employee identity

DATA MISUSE AND DAMAGE

Section M
1 d
2 c
3 a
4 a
5 b

Section Q
1 writeable CD, memory stick, tape. **Any 2**
2 change it regularly, don't choose something obvious, include numbers, don't write it down. **Any 3**
3 because new viruses are being produced all the time, these will not necessarily be picked up by existing anti virus programs
4 they can bring viruses into the company's computers, or other malicious software
5 valuable marketing data, can use it for promotions

Section E
1 a) in case the data is damaged or destroyed, it can then be restored
   b) in case the building is damaged by fire or burgled, the copy is unlikely to be lost as well
2 a) to reduce the risk of unauthorised access / tampering with the data, the fewer people with access, the lower the risk
   b) wasting company time, risk of downloading viruses, risk of spyware reporting company secrets. **Any 2**
3 a) (again) wasting time, risk of viruses
   b) a sacked employee might bear a grudge, and damage data / systems, quick removal prevents this risk. **Any 2**

DATA PRIVACY AND PROTECTION

Section M
1 c
2 c
3 a
4 c
5 d

Section Q
1 personal data can be widely available, anyone with an Internet connection can access sites that contain personal information
2 to provide protection / privacy /security, for personal data
3 the car seller, the finance company, the insurance company, the DVLA. **Any 3**
4 a) address, phone number, e-mail address, profession, (in some countries) criminal records. **Any 2**
   b) the electoral register
   c) use a search engine, turns up various websites, with published details about an individual. **Any 2**

Section E
1 a) search the electoral register, available on many subscription services, for a fee. **Any 2**
   b) the Data Protection Act has exemptions, there is no guarantee of privacy from government agencies
   c) the Data Protection Act, requires that data subjects can be aware of the data that is held on them
2 a) the computer company has passed on details to other companies, which have sent the junk mail using original details
   b) passing on information to other organisations, possible security breach
   c) show Fred the details stored, ensure good security on stored data, don't pass on details without permission / make sure that Fred agrees to passing on data for marketing purposes. **Any 2**

SYSTEMS DEVELOPMENT 1

Section M
1 c
2 a
3 a
4 a
5 c

Section Q
1 examples: upgrades needed, cabling, new computers, faster computers, more memory. **Any 3**
2 a) specially written, because it involves more work, much of it has to be set up from scratch. **Any 2**
   b) i) specially written: exactly suits requirements, can give specific instructions to programmers,
      ii) pre-existing: it is ready straightaway, thoroughly tested.
      2 marks, 1 from each section
3 data tables, user interface, output, input screens, documents, processes, links, menus. **Any 3**
4 breaking a problem down, into smaller parts

Section E
1 interviews, questionnaires, observations
2 examples: too expensive, staff can't (or won't) be retrained, will take too long, it might result in unacceptable redundancies. **Any 3**
3 a) the link between the user and the system, a way of interacting with the system, what the user sees and can work with. **Any 2 of these ideas**
   b) examples: menu, buttons, dialogue boxes, workspace, icons. **Any 2**
4 the layout of the pages, the links between the pages, the graphics to be used, interactive parts such as user feedback. **Any 3**

SYSTEMS DEVELOPMENT 2

Section M
1 a
2 a
3 d
4 b
5 d

Section Q
1 new ways of working, new hardware, to fix errors, to improve the way it looks or works. **Any 3**
2 users, developers, installers, system managers. **Any 2**
3 customising existing software, using wizards or other software generators, putting together pre-existing parts. **Any 2**
4 examples: in case of later disputes, in case they need to see what has been tested already, there may be clues about new faults in the results of old tests. **Any 2**
5 users trained, data prepared, new hardware installed, software installed. **Any 3**

Section E
1 a) examples: 1 should be accepted; any other number between 2 and 19 should be accepted; 0 should be rejected; 20 should be accepted; any number greater than 20 should be rejected; a non-number should be rejected. **Any 3 tests = 1 mark each, any 3 correct outcomes = 1 mark each**
   b) report an error
2 a) FAQs, troubleshooting guide, glossary, how to use it, how to save, how to make enquiries, tutorial. **Any 2**
   b) in case they need to change it, to fix faults, in case new programmers join the company. **Any 2**
3 Evaluation is checking that the software does what it is supposed to do, testing is to look for errors.
4 a) examples: new ways of working, new aspect to the business, updated the hardware, someone has suggested a better way for the system to work. **Any 1**
   b) the user/customer, the programmers, the analyst

WORD PROCESSING

Section M

1 c
2 b
3 a
4 b
5 b

Section Q

1 a) combinations of keys, that replace menu operations
   b) a more positive way to work, actions can be carried out more quickly. **Any 1**
2 A = style box
  B = font box
  C = font size box
  D = bold button
  E = left align button
3 to make text stand out, to indicate changes, to make the screen easier to see
4 What You See Is What You Get, it means that the screen display will look exactly the same when printed
5 producing many documents that are the same in many aspects, but have data from a database merged in, data merged into fields in the document

Section E

1 sans serif is good for headings, serif is good for body text, the tags help the eye along the text
2 a) a table, colours to make lines stand out
   b) a spreadsheet, also produces tables, but allows calculations, useful for working out intermediate times. **Any 2**
   c) write the letter with the word processor, enter fields for the customer details, merge the details from the database
3 a) highlight with shift and cursor keys, use keyboard shortcut, ctrl-b. **Any 2**
   b) the words are all 'legal' – in the dictionary, spell checker does not always warn of wrong usage
   c) search and replace

DESKTOP PUBLISHING

Section M

1 b
2 a
3 c
4 b
5 d

Section Q

1 text is imported, graphics are imported, page is designed using DTP, layout is the main job of DTP. **Any 2**
2 a basic design on which new documents are based, it saves time in setting up a new page, it can help produce a good design if the user is not good at designs. **Any 2**
3 examples: newsletters, business cards, flyers, CD covers, letterheads, compliment slips, certificates. **Any 3**
4 they contain text/graphics, they can be moved about the page, or off it, text can be flowed round them. **Any 2**
5 a hyperlink

Section E

1 a) 4
   b) use a digital camera, upload the graphics file onto the computer, import it into the DTP package, use an ordinary camera, scan the image, import the graphics file into the DTP package. **Any 4 points**
2 a) use a word processor
   b) it has features specially designed for text preparations, such as search and replace, grammar checkers etc. **Any 2**
3 a) lacks most features for web page construction, HTML code produced is messy and difficult to edit
   b) use web authoring software, or a text editor, or call in a specialist. **Any 2**
   c) website is interactive (DTP document is not), website subject to download constraints (DTP is designed as hard copy). **Any 2 reasonable differences**

SPREADSHEETS 1

Section M

1 a
2 b
3 c
4 a
5 c

Section Q

1 A1
2 ctrl-home
3 a worksheet is one page, the workbook is the whole spreadsheet file
4 format cells currency, select dollars
5 a) because numbers default to the right (or text defaults to the left)
   b) highlight cells, click align button

Section E

1 enter 'Jan', click on cell autofill button, drag across range. **Any 2**
2 a) fill right, fill series, copy and paste. **Any 2**
   b) correct the alignment, embolden headings, use currency format. **Any 2**
3 keep it on a separate sheet, in the same workbook
4 highlight area, format – autoformat, select a suitable style
5 highlight area, autoformat, choose style

SPREADSHEETS 2

Section M

1 a
2 d
3 c
4 c
5 d

Section Q

1 a formula is made from basic relationships between operators and data, a function is a pre-packaged and named collection of actions
2 a) 34
   b) 54
   c) 22
   d) 1.5
   e) 5.5
3 4
4 =A2
5 =$A$1
6 absolute cell addressing, they stop the references changing when copying

Section E

1 a) =2*F1*A2
   b) =F1*A2^2
   c) the formulae would adjust as they are copied, this would stop them referring to the value of pi.
   d) use absolute cell addressing, change F1 to F$1 or $F$1, this would stop the reference adjusting when copied
   e) give it a name
   f) =IF(C2>100,"big enough","too small")
   g) =MAX(B2:C11)

SPREADSHEETS 3

Section M

1 d
2 c
3 b
4 a
5 b

Section Q

1 spreadsheet is a flat file database, relational database has more than one table, linked by key fields. **Any 2**
2 highlight the names and the marks, set the filter in the mark column, to >50
3 a) a form
   b) data area highlighted, then form selected

Section E

1 a stored set of actions, in an application, that can be replayed whenever required. **Any 2**
2 so that actions are replayed accurately, to save effort
3 a) ctrl-z
   b) Circumference of a circle
   c) on Sheet 2 (on the spreadsheet)
   d) a scatter chart
   e) range A2:B11
3 by recording the macro, by going through the necessary actions

MODELS & SIMULATIONS

Section M
1 b
2 c
3 d
4 c
5 d

Section Q
1 not knowing the rules, insufficient data
2 real-life event may be: too quick, too slow, too expensive, too dangerous, inaccessible. **Any 3**
3 can try out sizes/shapes, without the trouble of doing this in reality, more options available
4 a means of determining when it is cooked, timings, sizes, temperature. **Any 2**
5 a model is a set of rules/relationships, a simulation is a representation of reality based on a model

Section E
1 a way to calculate the cost of paint, based on the areas given
2 area, cost of paint, how much paint is needed per unit area
3 cost per hour, how many hours required
4 a) examples: insert new item, remove item, rotate item, change views, change colour/texture, calculate costs. **Any 3**
   b) size of kitchen, what units are wanted, how many of each unit wanted, position of each unit. **Any 3**
   c) details of units available: their sizes, costs, shapes, colours. **Any 3**

DATA-LOGGING

Section M
1 c
2 a
3 b
4 b
5 b

Section Q
1 a) temperature
   b) somewhere between 1 second and 1 minute
   c) somewhere between half an hour and 3 hours
2 a) pH
   b) proximity/light sensor
   c) pressure/magnetic/light sensor
3 a) table, graph
   b) spreadsheet
4 more accurate, can log over longer period, short periods can be better sampled, data might be in remote place, or dangerous location. **Any 3**

Section E
1 a) to give data to the taxi meter to calculate fares, to log distance covered for calculating when service due
   b) on a memory chip / writeable ROM (not disk)
   c) less than a second – approx a tenth of a second or less
   d) to see trends in vehicle use, to decide when services due
2 a) they can check the status of many components, without having to examine them, can locate errors, speed up servicing / error diagnostics. **Any 2**
   b) can store data for looking at later, can use it to display suitable message on screen, can help with diagnostics. **Any 2**
   c) more to go wrong, possibly expensive to replace logging equipment, need specialist equipment / software to track down faults. **Any 2**
3 a) the opening of the bag, the deceleration of the car on impact
   b) events happen too quickly for human measurement, can be dangerous for humans to do the measurements

PROGRAMMING AND CONTROL

Section M
1 a
2 b
3 d
4 c
5 a

Section Q
1 a) less likely to make mistakes with small pieces, easier to test, easier to understand. **Any 2**
   b) procedure, function
2 they don't get tired, don't go on strike, they can repeat actions without mistakes, they are accurate, they are often cheaper than humans. **Any 3**
3 robot is programmable, it can carry out different functions automatically
4 a set of instructions, for a computer to carry out
5 examples: microwave oven, washing machine, dishwasher, video/DVD/CD player. **Any 3**

Section E
1 only a simple job to do, cheaper than a computer, no need to re-program very often. **Any 2**
2 a) detect_floor, move_to
   b) floor_no, floor_at
   c) someone presses a button
   d) nothing
   e) nothing (again)
   f) the lift goes to floor 2

MULTIMEDIA

Section M
1 a
2 d
3 c
4 c
5 a

Section Q
1 text, graphics, sound, moving images. **Any 3**
2 because the media concerned are all moving towards digital storage, that makes it easier to work with them together
3 multimedia is more striking than single media, people find it more memorable, more interesting, more different situations can be portrayed. **Any 2**
4 images/movies/sound make big files, DVDs hold a lot of data, they are portable, more feasible to carry presentations around. **Any 3**
5 click on links, watch movies, play sounds, use search facility. **Any 2**

Section E
1 films of heart beats/circulation, stills of blood cells, sounds of heart beats etc, animations. **Any 2**
2 video recorder, television, overhead projector. **Any 2**
3 websites, multimedia encyclopaedias, own films, own photographs, scans from publications. **Any 3**
4 the resources may be copyright, permission must be obtained first
5 pupils might find it more interesting, they are used to this approach on the web and on television, more can be covered. **Any 2**
6 use a data projector, send it to each workstation in a room of networked computers

PRESENTATIONS

Section M
1 b
2 c
3 b
4 d
5 a

Section Q
1 keeps the speaker on track, makes the points more clearly, keeps the audience focused, summarises the main points, keeps audience interest. **Any 3**
2 keep them simple, use few fonts, choose non-clashing colours, not too many bullet points per slide, have a consistent look. **Any 3**
3 a set of rules for documents or other communications, that makes them recognisably from a particular company
4 all or most of the slides are based on a common design, therefore they have a common look
5 a self-running presentation

Section E
1 to attract the customers' attention
2 a) because the shoppers will not want to waste time standing around, so need to have a show with much impact
   b) must have fast processors, as movies involve a lot of changes in images, need a lot of storage/RAM/disk space, because movies are large files. **Any 2**
3 a) less use of movies, more text, not self-timed, contains summaries. **Any 3**
   b) put it on a master slide, this will appear on every slide
   c) use the slide sorter, to drag slides to new position
   d) focuses the audience on each point as it is being made.

NETWORKS

Section M
1 a
2 a
3 d
4 c
5 c

Section Q
1 printers can be shared, so fewer need to be bought
2 examples: store data files, store programs, connect to printers / other shared peripherals, control logins, keep a log of activities. **Any 3**
3 cable (fibre or metal), radio
4 to connect a computer/network, to another network
5 because they need specialist staff to maintain, there is always work to be done on them

Section E
1 records can be transferred, from receptionist to treatment room, details of treatment can be transferred to receptionist, bills prepared more quickly. **Any 2**
2 they can communicate with each other more easily, access to patient records from any room
3 a network interface card (NIC)
4 LAN, because it is on one site
5 to identify who they are, to ensure that unauthorised people do not gain access, to establish a connection with the server. **Any 2**
6 a) router (or modem)
   b) risk of acquiring viruses which may damage data, risk of being hacked into and compromising security of patient records
7 paying someone to install the network, maintenance costs – to sort out problems, develop the network. **Any 2**

THE INTERNET

Section M
1 c
2 a
3 c
4 c
5 b

Section Q
1 World Wide Web, e-mail, file transfer
2 a web server
3 a) a means of transmission, where many signals can be sent simultaneously, thereby allowing fast data transfer. **Any 2**
   b) digital
   c) asynchronous digital subscriber line, can work with existing phone
4 text with highlighted words, that form links, to other locations.

Section E
1 makes it a heading, the largest heading style
2 a) the cat image (Cleo), the word 'cat'
   b) page2.htm
3 http
4 riversidepets.org
5 a) some users might only have slow modems, pictures take a long time to download
   b) they are broadband users, the pictures will download quickly

E-MAIL

Section M
1 d
2 c
3 c
4 d
5 b

Section Q
1 a) larger storage capacity, larger / no limits on message size
   b) can access it anywhere, has other online services included, no need to worry about losing mails because of computer failure. **Any 2**
2 a) unwanted e-mails, usually sent in bulk
   b) more spam, because replying confirms that the e-mail address exists
3 a) applets
   b) animations of the cars, can view from all sides, can change colours, can change accessories. **Any 2**
4 briefcase/storage area, chat/discussion/special interest groups, the news, a diary. **Any 2**

Section E
1 E
2 the address book will open
3 the e-mail is confidential / so that unauthorised people cannot read it
4 the address of other people to send the e-mail to
5 A
6 B
7 to attach a separate computer file to the message
8 the mails would not carry the right return address, the company would not have suitable records of e-mails sent

This is an exam-style question. Answer all parts of the question.

Herb runs a garden centre. He sells plants and gardening equipment. All his stock is bar coded. He has software that works at the point of sale and also tracks what items he has in stock.

Sometimes, when goods are being scanned, the bar code number is not read correctly and a warning is sounded.

1 a) Explain why a bar code scan might lead to a warning being sounded.

....

.... (3 marks)

b) How can a checkout operator register a sale if the bar code is not read properly?

.... (2 marks)

2 Some customers pay by credit card. These cards carry information that can be read by machine.
a) State two alternative ways that credit cards can carry machine-readable information.

.... (2 marks)

b) Apart from a point of sale terminal, what extra hardware will be needed to deal with credit card payments?

.... (1 mark)

3 When employees arrive at Herb's Garden Centre, they have to use a card to open the car park barrier.
a) What advantage does this system have for the employees?

.... (2 marks)

b) What data needs to be encoded on this card?

.... (2 marks)

Score .... /12

TOTAL SCORE   /30

DATA MISUSE AND DAMAGE

M Choose just one answer, a, b, c or d.

1 A program that installs itself on a PC's hard disk, disguised as something else, is called
  a) a virus   b) a worm
  c) spyware   d) a Trojan horse.

2 A virus is always
  a) a program that always causes damage to data files
  b) an attachment to an e-mail
  c) a program that copies itself
  d) a program that spies on your computer activities.

3 Hacking is often defined as
  a) unauthorised access to a computer system
  b) damaging data
  c) writing viruses
  d) installing spyware.

4 A firewall
  a) prevents access to a private computer from outside
  b) encrypts data
  c) blocks viruses
  d) prevents damage to data.

5 In order to understand encrypted data it is necessary to have
  a) the original encryption software
  b) the key
  c) the password to the file
  d) a suitable level of access.

Score .... /5

Q Answer all parts of all questions.

1 State two ways to back up a large quantity of data that are suitable for a home computer user.

.... (2 marks)

2 Give three good rules that you should follow concerning your network password.

.... (3 marks)

3 Why should anti-virus software be updated regularly?

.... (2 marks)

4 Why do many companies make the bringing in of floppy disks a sackable offence?

.... (2 marks)

5 Why might a company find the customer details of another company useful?

.... (2 marks)

Score .... /11

E This is an exam-style question. Answer all parts of the question.

J & M is a large company of stockbrokers. They buy and sell shares on behalf of their clients. They have 500 employees who work with a network of computers that gives access to the latest share prices. Their customer details are stored on a database on a server that is linked to their network.

Every day, the client database is backed up onto a tape. This tape is taken to a separate building for storage.

1 a) Explain why the client data has to be backed up.

....

.... (2 marks)

b) Explain why the tape is taken to another building for storage.

....

.... (2 marks)

2 a) Only the staff who deal with the customers are given access to the customer database. Explain why this is so.

....

.... (2 marks)

b) The staff are not allowed to use the Internet except for share dealing. Why does the company insist on this?

....

.... (2 marks)

3 Recently, one of the customer service staff was caught installing games onto the company's computers from a floppy disk. He was immediately dismissed and escorted off the premises.
a) Why was installing a game considered a sackable offence?

....

.... (2 marks)

b) Why was the employee escorted off the premises straightaway rather than given notice?

....

.... (2 marks)

Score .... /12

TOTAL SCORE   /28

For more help on this topic see KS3 ICT Success Guide pages 38–39

DATA PRIVACY AND PROTECTION

M Choose just one answer, a, b, c or d.

1 Which of these is a part of the UK Data Protection Act?
a) personal details must not be used for accounting purposes
b) personal details must not be used for statistical purposes
c) personal details must be kept securely
d) personal details must not be passed on to other companies under any circumstances

2 A person who is responsible for looking after personal details on a company's computer system is called a
a) data subject b) data commissioner
c) data controller d) data registrar.

3 A person whose personal details are recorded on a computer system is called a
a) data subject b) data user
c) data controller d) data item.

4 Which of these is a legal use of personal data obtained when someone fills in a loan application form?
a) The data is used in the company's advertising.
b) The data is sold to a different company so it can send marketing material.
c) The data is used to remind the customer of an overdue payment.
d) The data is passed to the company's partners in other countries not subject to a Data Protection Act.

5 Privacy is more of a problem with IT systems than with paper systems because
a) data on IT systems is more accurate
b) data on IT systems is more personal
c) data on IT systems is more widely available
d) it is easy to combine data from various sources with IT systems.

Score .... /5

Q Answer all parts of all questions.

1 Explain how the Internet can be a threat to personal privacy.

.... (2 marks)

2 What is the basic purpose of the Data Protection Act?

.... (2 marks)

3 Someone buys a car using credit. Give three organisations that will collect personal data on the purchaser.

.... (3 marks)

4 a) Give two details about someone's personal life that can very easily be found from Internet searches.

.... (2 marks)

b) What source of personal information in the UK, previously only available in local areas, is now available for Internet searching to anyone?

.... (1 mark)

c) Describe one other way in which people can use the Internet to find out details about someone's life.

.... (2 marks)

Score .... /12

E | **This is an exam-style question. Answer all parts of the question.**

Fred has just finished writing a book. His publishers have paid him an advance and the details of the book are recorded on a database under its ISBN number. Fred has also produced a website containing some of the ideas that he has written in his book. Later on, he receives royalties – a percentage from the sales of the book.

1 a) Explain how someone could find Fred's postal address from the available information.

.... (3 marks)

b) The Inland Revenue wants to take a large amount of Fred's earnings away from him in tax. Fred thinks that they won't know what he has earned and that he is safe under the Data Protection Act from their enquiries. Explain why this is not the case.

.... (2 marks)

c) Every year, Fred's publisher sends him a printed record of the data that they hold about him. Explain why they have to do this.

.... (2 marks)

2 Fred buys a new computer and fills in a registration document. He accidentally makes a mistake in spelling his street name. Later on, he gets lots of junk mail from different companies which include the mis-spelling.
a) How has this happened?

.... (2 marks)

b) Fred thinks that the Data Protection Act has been breached. Suggest two aspects that could have been breached here?

.... (2 marks)

c) What steps should the computer company have taken to avoid any problems of this sort?

.... (2 marks)

Score .... /13

TOTAL SCORE   /30

For more help on this topic see KS3 ICT Success Guide pages 40–41

SYSTEMS DEVELOPMENT 1

M Choose just one answer, a, b, c or d.

1 All of these jobs can be done on a computer. Which of them is the most suitable for computer processing?
   a) writing a short note
   b) adding up a shopping bill
   c) monitoring air temperature outside an aircraft in flight
   d) planning a vegetable garden

2 The person who helps a business to work out a new computer solution to a problem is a
   a) systems analyst
   b) systems administrator
   c) systems technician
   d) systems operator.

3 When planning a new system, which of these is the most important consideration?
   a) output   b) input
   c) processing   d) the user interface

4 Interviewing the user of a planned system to find out what is wanted in a new system is mostly done by the
   a) analyst   b) programmer
   c) project manager d) designer.

5 If data tables are needed in a computer solution, their layout is planned during which stage?
   a) analysis   b) feasibility study
   c) design   d) implementation.

Score .... /5

Q Answer all parts of all questions.

1 A new system is planned by a company. Give three decisions that might have to be taken about hardware.

   .... (3 marks)

2 a) Software can be specially written or produced from a pre-existing program such as Microsoft Access. Which is more expensive to obtain, a specially written program or a pre-existing program? Explain your answer.

   .... (2 marks)

   b) Apart from cost issues, give one advantage of getting (i) specially written software and (ii) pre-existing software.

   .... (2 marks)

3 State three things that have to be designed during the development of software.

   .... (3 marks)

4 What is top-down design?

   .... (2 marks)

Score .... /12

This is an exam-style question. Answer all parts of the question.

Cedric runs Cedric's Travel, which is a bus company. The company runs buses throughout a county. They plan services, buy and maintain their vehicles and employ over 50 people. All their activities could benefit from a complete information management system. They invite in a software development company to help them to organise their business better.

1 State three ways in which the software company can get the information it needs to solve Cedric's problems.

....

....

.... (3 marks)

2 After carefully investigating the problem, the software company presents some conclusions to Cedric before proceeding with the plans. It is possible that Cedric might decide not to proceed with the information management system.
Give three reasons why the plan might be abandoned at this stage.

....

....

.... (3 marks)

3 Cedric decides to go ahead with the new scheme, but his staff are concerned that they will be unable to cope with it. The developers assure Cedric that the user interface will be easy to understand.
a) What is the user interface?

.... (2 marks)

b) State two components that there might be in a user interface.

.... (2 marks)

4 Cedric decides that he would like a website as well, to advertise his business. State three aspects of the website that will have to be designed.

....

....

.... (3 marks)

Score .... /13

TOTAL SCORE   /30

For more help on this topic see KS3 ICT Success Guide pages 42–43

SYSTEMS DEVELOPMENT 2

M — Choose just one answer, a, b, c or d.

1 When a computer system is produced, it is tested by the developers. Which of these is a reason why the customer will also need to do some testing?
   a) the customer might make a mistake that the developers did not think of
   b) it will save time
   c) it will save money
   d) the testers might have left the developer's company

2 Some documentation takes the user through an example of how to work with the system, step by step. This is
   a) a tutorial   b) a troubleshooting guide
   c) a glossary   d) an installation guide.

3 Which of these ways of providing user documentation is the easiest to update?
   a) a book   b) a CD
   c) online help packaged with the software
   d) web-based

4 Changing a computer system after it has been delivered is called
   a) implementation   b) maintenance
   c) roll out   d) evaluation.

5 Checking to see that a new system does everything that was originally required is called
   a) implementation
   b) maintenance
   c) roll out
   d) evaluation.

Score .... /5

Q — Answer all parts of all questions.

1 Give three reasons why software might be changed after it has been in use for a while.

   .... (3 marks)

2 Name two types of people who will need to have documentation about a computer solution.

   .... (2 marks)

3 Not all new computer systems are programmed from scratch. How else might they be produced?

   .... (2 marks)

4 Why is it important that software testers keep records of what they do?

   .... (2 marks)

5 Describe three activities that might take place when a new software system is introduced into a company.

   .... (3 marks)

Score .... /12

This is an exam-style question. Answer all parts of the question.

When the new system was being developed for Cedric's Travel, one part of it looked up service details about each of their buses. They have 20 buses, numbered from 1 to 20.

1 a) Suggest three items of data that the testers could use to make sure that only valid numbers could be input. For each item, state what the test result should be.

....

....

....

....

....(6 marks)

b) What should the system do if the user inputs wrong data?

.... (1 mark)

2 a) The users are provided with a user manual to help them get the best out of the system. State two sections that will be in this manual.

....

.... (2 marks)

b) The software developers also keep documentation about the new system. Why might they need this in the future?

.... (2 marks)

3 When the system is delivered, Cedric and his staff evaluate it. How is evaluation different from testing?

.... (2 marks)

4 Later, Cedric decides that the software needs updating.
a) Give one reason why this might happen.

.... (1 mark)

b) Who needs to be involved in this process of updating?

....

.... (3 marks)

Score .... /17

TOTAL SCORE   /34

WORD PROCESSING

M **Choose just one answer, a, b, c or d.**

1 In a word processor, a combination of font, size, colour and spacing is called a
  a) format   b) template
  c) style   d) font.

2 When text is removed from one location and repositioned somewhere else in a document, it is called
  a) copy and paste   b) cut and paste
  c) find and replace d) drag and drop.

3 The first paragraph of section E (page 47) is
  a) aligned left   b) aligned centre
  c) aligned right   d) justified.

4 A sans serif font
  a) has tags on the letters
  b) has no tags on the letters
  c) is sloping
  d) is particularly large.

5 *This question has been printed in*
  a) bold, italic, sans serif
  b) bold, italic, serif
  c) not bold, italic, serif
  d) not bold, normal, serif.

Score .... /5

Q **Answer all parts of all questions.**

1 a) In word processing, what are keyboard shortcuts?

.... (2 marks)

  b) Why do many word processor users prefer to use keyboard shortcuts instead of the mouse?

.... (1 mark)

2 This is part of a word processor screen. Identify the parts A–E.

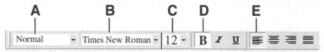

.... (5 marks)

3 Give three reasons why someone might want to use colour when word processing a document apart from wanting the document to print in colour.

.... (3 marks)

4 What is WYSIWYG and why is it important?

.... (2 marks)

5 What is mail merge?

.... (3 marks)

Score .... /16

This is an exam-style question. Answer all parts of the question.

Cedric's Travel wants to make a corporate image for itself. It wants all its letters, invoices and advertisements to have a consistent look.
Cedric decides that the heading on his headed notepaper will be set out in a sans serif font called Verdana. The letters will be typed in the serif font Times New Roman.

1   Suggest why this is a good choice of fonts in this case.

    .... (2 marks)

2   Cedric wants to send a personal letter to all his previous customers, announcing some timetable changes that the company is planning.
    a) State two features of a word processor that could be used to make a neat bus timetable?

    .... (2 marks)

    b) What alternative software might be a better choice for this purpose? Give a reason for your choice.

    .... (2 marks)

    c) Cedric has all his customers' details stored on his new Information Management database. How can he use a word processor to send a personal letter to each of them?

    .... (3 marks)

3   Cedric types out the new timetable. Some of the times have to be printed in bold so that he can indicate exceptions such as Saturdays only.

The Quay	12.30
The Post Office	12.41
The Station	12.50
Cross Roads	**13.05 so**
Hospital	13.10
School	13.15
so Saturdays only	

    a) Every time, he enters a time in bold, he highlights it with the mouse and clicks on a button on the menu. He is getting fed up with this as it makes his hands ache. What better way is there to do this?

    .... (2 marks)

    b) Cedric gets his Saturday helper to make a flyer with the word processor. He wants the name of the company and the logo, plus the slogan 'We take you there in style'. Unfortunately, his helper can't spell and types 'We take you their in stile'. He gets no warning from the spell checker and prints 1000 copies.
        Explain why the word processor did not warn of this mistake.

    .... (2 marks)

    c) The helper has made the same mistake lots of times in another document. Explain how he can change all the wrong spellings to the correct ones without retyping every one.

    .... (1 mark)

    Score .... /14

TOTAL SCORE   /35

For more help on this topic see KS3 ICT Success Guide pages 48–49

DESKTOP PUBLISHING

M Choose just one answer, a, b, c or d.

1 When you make business cards with DTP software, you can answer a set of questions and the software then sets the cards out according to your wishes. This is an example of a
   a) template   b) wizard
   c) design   d) master page.

2 DTP software is much better than word processing software for
   a) laying out a page
   b) entering lots of text
   c) checking grammar
   d) producing a table of contents.

3 In which of these ways is a web page different from a DTP document?
   a) web pages use graphics
   b) web pages include text
   c) web pages can be interactive
   d) web pages can be based on templates

4 The process of bringing in a word processed text file to a DTP document is called
   a) pasting   b) importing
   c) exporting   d) linking.

5 A unit on a DTP page that holds text or graphics is called
   a) a holder   b) a control
   c) a picture   d) a frame.

Score .... /5

Q Answer all parts of all questions.

1 Give two basic functions of DTP software that distinguish it from word processing software?

.... (2 marks)

2 In DTP, what is a template and why is it useful?

.... (2 marks)

3 Give three examples of documents that can be set up with a DTP wizard.

.... (3 marks)

4 Explain how frames can help to set up a page.

.... (2 marks)

5 What feature can be added to a DTP document to make it interactive, if the document is to be converted into a web page?

.... (1 mark)

Score .... /10

This is an exam-style question. Answer all parts of the question.

Cedric's Travel now has a new IT system and is ready to take on more business. Cedric wants to produce lots of advertisements and has decided to use DTP software to help him make some professional looking material.
Here is the first version of a flyer.

1 a) How many frames are on this flyer?

.... (1 mark)

   b) Cedric wants to replace the picture of the coach with a photograph of one of his buses.
       Describe two ways that can he do this.

.... (4 marks)

2 Cedric wants to write a feature for his local paper. It will have a lot of text in it describing
   what has been happening in the company and it will also have some pictures.
   a) What is the best way of preparing the text for the feature?

.... (1 mark)

   b) Give a reason for your answer in (a)

.... (2 marks)

3 Cedric notices that his DTP software has a Save As Website option. He thinks that this will
   be a cheap way to set up a good website to advertise his business on the Internet.
   a) Explain why this is probably not a good idea.

.... (2 marks)

   b) What should he do instead to produce a good website?

.... (2 marks)

   c) What differences are there between producing a good DTP document and producing a
       good website?

.... (2 marks)

Score .... /14

TOTAL SCORE   /29

For more help on this topic see KS3 ICT Success Guide pages 50–51

SPREADSHEETS 1

M Choose just one answer, a, b, c or d.

1 One cell on a spreadsheet has a thick box around it to show where the typing will go. This cell is called the
a) active cell b) working cell
c) lookup cell d) current cell.

2 Someone types a sum of money into a spreadsheet cell like this: $34.50. The spreadsheet is set up in British format. The spreadsheet will then take this data to be
a) a number b) text
c) currency d) a cell reference.

3 A cell contains a calculated number with too many decimal places. The number of decimal places showing can be reduced by
a) narrowing the column
b) auto formatting the cell

c) using the format cell option
d) deleting some of the digits.

4 The number .50 is entered into a spreadsheet cell. Unless someone changes the options, it will display as
a) .5 b) 0.5
c) 00.5 d) 5

5 The number .5 is entered into a spreadsheet cell and the format option is set to percent. The display will now be
a) .5% b) 5%
c) 50% d) 500%

Score .... /5

Q Answer all parts of all questions.

1 What are the coordinates of the top-left cell in a spreadsheet?

.... (1 mark)

2 What keyboard action takes you to the top-left cell from anywhere?

.... (1 mark)

3 What is the difference between a worksheet and a workbook?

.... (2 marks)

4 What action would you take to display a sum of money in dollars on a spreadsheet?

.... (1 mark)

5 Here is a list of data in a spreadsheet that has been typed in without changing any formats.

Name	Exam mark
Gus	12
Max	56
Michelle	48
Stephanie	67

a) Why is the alignment of the marks column wrong?

.... (1 mark)

b) How would you correct this?

.... (2 marks)

Score .... /8

E | **This is an exam-style question. Answer all parts of the question.**

Lou is a businessman who is having some financial worries. He needs to estimate what his expenses will be for the next year. He sets up a spreadsheet and wants the months of the year to appear along one row.

Jan	Feb	Mar	Apr	May	Jun

1 Explain how can he do this without typing them all in.

.... (2 marks)

2 He spends about £50 a month on petrol so he wants to enter that into the spreadsheet.

A	B	C	D	E	F
Jan	Feb	Mar	Apr	May	Jun
50	50	50	50	50	50

a) Describe two ways he can do this without typing in the 50 for every month.

.... (2 marks)

b) Describe two things he could now do to improve the display.

.... (2 marks)

3 Lou also wants to keep a record of what he has sold each month. He wants to keep this separate from his expenses but does not want to start a new spreadsheet. Describe the best way to do this.

.... (2 marks)

4 Lou knows that he can display money with the currency symbols from different countries, but he has forgotten how to do this. Describe how the spreadsheet software can help him find out what he needs to know.

.... (2 marks)

5 Lou adds some more to the spreadsheet and improves the appearance so that it looks like this:

	A	B	C	D	E	F	G
1	Expenses						
2		Jan	Feb	Mar	Apr	May	Jun
3	Petrol	£ 50.00	£ 60.00	£ 70.00	£ 70.00	£ 65.00	£ 65.00
4	Electricity	£ 50.00	£ 50.00	£ 60.00	£ 60.00	£ 70.00	£ 80.00
5	Council Tax	£150.00	£150.00	£150.00	£150.00	£150.00	£150.00

Describe how Lou used an automated feature of the spreadsheet to make this improved display.

.... (3 marks)

Score .... /13

TOTAL SCORE /26

For more help on this topic see KS3 ICT Success Guide pages 52–53

SPREADSHEETS 2

M **Choose just one answer, a, b, c or d.**

1 The car registration AW52AAA is entered into a spreadsheet cell. The spreadsheet will take this to be which of the following?
   a) text   b) number
   c) a formula   d) special

2 If a spreadsheet entry starts with an equals sign, the spreadsheet will
   a) take it as text   b) take it as a number
   c) take it as a date   d) attempt to perform a process on it.

3 This is part of a spreadsheet used to determine bonuses for the sales staff of a company.

	A	B	C
1	Sales (units)	Sales person	Result
2			
3	45	Jones	below target
4	49	Smith	below target
5	50	Johns	below target
6	51	Timmins	102
7	55	George	110
8			

The entry in cell C3 is
   a) =IF(A4>50,A3*2,"below target")
   b) =IF(A3>50,102,"below target")
   c) =IF(A3>50,A3*2,"below target")
   d) =IF(A3>50,110,"below target").

4 In the same spreadsheet, the function =MIN(A3:A7) is entered into cell A8. What will appear in cell A8 as a result?
   a) =MIN(A3:A7)   b) 0
   c) 45   d) 55

5 In another cell on the same spreadsheet, someone enters =C6+C7*10. This cell will then show
   a) 212   b) 21200
   c) 21.2   d) 1202

Score .... /5

Q **Answer all parts of all questions.**

1 In a spreadsheet, what is the difference between a formula and a function?

.... (2 marks)

2 This is part of a spreadsheet.

What would be displayed in cell A5 if each of the following were entered into that cell?

	A
1	4
2	5
3	6
4	7
5	

a) =A1+A2*A3 .... (1 mark)

b) =(A1+A2)*A3 .... (1 mark)

c) =SUM(A1:A4) .... (1 mark)

d) =(A1+A2)/A3 .... (1 mark)

e) =AVERAGE(A1:A4) .... (1 mark)

3 The value =A1 is typed into cell B1. What will be displayed in cell B1? .... (1 mark)

Q Continued

4 Autofill is used to drag the contents of cell B1 into cell B2.
What will the formula be in cell B2? .... (1 mark)

5 The value in cell B1 is changed to =$A$1. This is then copied down to cell B2 by using autofill. What will be the new formula in cell B2? .... (1 mark)

6 What is the meaning of the dollar symbols in the formula =$A$1? .... (1 mark)

Score .... /11

E This is an exam-style question. Answer all parts of the question.

The formula to calculate the circumference of a circle is 2πr. r is the radius of the circle.
The formula to calculate the area of a circle is πr². The value of π (pi) can be approximated to 3.142.
A spreadsheet is used to calculate the circumferences and areas of ten circles.
The radius of the circles goes up in steps from 1 to 10.

	A	B	C	D	E	F
1	radius	circumference	area		pi	3.142
2	1	6.284	3.142			
3	2	12.568	12.568			
4	3	18.852	28.278			
5	4	25.136	50.272			
6	5	31.42	78.55			
7	6	37.704	113.112			
8	7	43.988	153.958			
9	8	50.272	201.088			
10	9	56.556	254.502			
11	10	62.84	314.2			
12						

The value of pi is entered into cell F1.

a) What formula is entered into cell B2? .... (1 mark)

b) What formula is entered into cell C2? .... (1 mark)

c) If the formulae in cells B2 and C2 were copied down using autofill, the wrong results would occur. Explain why.

.... (2 marks)

d) Explain how changes could be made to the formulae in cells B2 and C2 in order to avoid this problem?

.... (2 marks)

e) State another way of referring to a cell apart from using its coordinates.

.... (1 mark)

f) What formula can be put into cell D2 and then copied down, to report which areas are greater than 100. If they are, the cell should contain the entry *big enough*, otherwise it should say *too small*.

.... (2 marks)

g) What function could be entered into cell F3 to report the largest figure in the

whole range? .... (1 mark)

Score .... /10

TOTAL SCORE /26

For more help on this topic see KS3 ICT Success Guide pages 54–55

SPREADSHEETS 3

M Choose just one answer, a, b, c or d.

1 A survey is carried out to find out how many students in a school have each eye colour. The results are entered into a spreadsheet and a chart is produced. The most suitable type of chart for this is a
a) bar chart   b) column chart
c) line graph   d) pie chart.

2 Another chart is plotted to show how the temperature of the air changed during the course of the day. Readings were taken every 30 minutes. The best way to display these results graphically is a
a) bar chart   b) column chart
c) line graph   d) pie chart.

3 A chart can be produced very quickly in a spreadsheet by using a
a) template   b) wizard
c) style   d) master chart.

4 The data in a spreadsheet is needed in a database so it is saved in a format that the database can use. This process is called
a) exporting data   b) formatting data
c) pasting data   d) embedding data.

5 Spreadsheets can be useful as simple databases. In this case, one row is equivalent to a database
a) table   b) record
c) field   d) file.

Score .... /5

Q Answer all parts of all questions.

1 Spreadsheets can be used to store data, but they are limited compared with specialised database management systems. How does a relational database differ from a spreadsheet data file?

.... (2 marks)

2 A spreadsheet contains the names and test marks of all the students in a class. How could you use the spreadsheet to display the names and marks of those students who scored more than 50?

.... (3 marks)

3 A spreadsheet can be set up to make it easier for someone to enter data so that it looks like this:

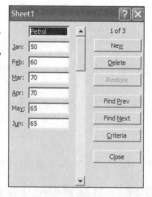

Q Continued

a) What is this feature called?

.... (1 mark)

b) How is this feature set up so that it connects with the correct data on the spreadsheet?

.... (2 marks)

Score .... /8

E This is an exam-style question. Answer all parts of the question.

Fred is a mathematician and he wants to show on a graph some details about the sizes of circles. He produces a macro to do this.

1 What is a macro?

.... (2 marks)

2 Give two reasons why macros can be useful.

.... (2 marks)

3 Fred produces the macro which is shown here.

```
Sub Macro1()
'
' Macro1 Macro
' Macro recorded 25/07/2004 by Fred Bloggs
'
' Keyboard Shortcut: Ctrl+z
'
    Range("A2:B11").Select
    Charts.Add
    ActiveChart.ChartType = xlXYScatterSmooth
    ActiveChart.SetSourceData Source:=Sheets("Sheet2").Range("A2:B11"), PlotBy _
        :=xlColumns
    ActiveChart.Location Where:=xlLocationAsObject, Name:="Sheet2"
    With ActiveChart
        .HasTitle = True
        .ChartTitle.Characters.Text = "Circumference of a circle"
        .Axes(xlCategory, xlPrimary).HasTitle = True
        .Axes(xlCategory, xlPrimary).AxisTitle.Characters.Text = "circumference"
        .Axes(xlValue, xlPrimary).HasTitle = True
        .Axes(xlValue, xlPrimary).AxisTitle.Characters.Text = "radius"
    End With
End Sub
```

a) How can Fred activate this macro by one keyboard action?

.... (1 mark)

b) What will the title be on a chart that this macro produces? .... (1 mark)

c) When the macro is run, where will the chart appear? .... (1 mark)

d) What type of chart will this macro produce? .... (1 mark)

e) From which cells on the spreadsheet will the macro get its data? .... (1 mark)

3 Fred did not have to write the program code shown here. Explain how he was able to produce this macro without having to do that.

.... (2 marks)

Score .... /11

TOTAL SCORE /24

For more help on this topic see KS3 ICT Success Guide pages 56–57

MODELS AND SIMULATIONS

M **Choose just one answer, a, b, c or d.**

1 Which of these types of software is most likely to be used to make a model?
   a) graphics software
   b) a spreadsheet
   c) a word processor
   d) desktop publishing

2 Which of these is likely to be the output from a model?
   a) yesterday's air temperature
   b) the temperature at which water freezes
   c) tomorrow's wind speed
   d) the increase in temperature over the last month

3 Which of these is a good reason to set up a computer model of a real-life situation?
   a) The real-life situation is never likely to occur.
   b) There is insufficient data in the real-life situation.
   c) The real-life situation is not properly understood.
   d) The real-life situation would take too long.

4 Which of these makes use of a simulation?
   a) working out how much cardboard it will take to make a box
   b) finding the area of a circle whose radius is known
   c) a computer game that uses virtual reality
   d) producing a graph from a formula

5 Which of these situations where modelling is used is most likely to produce correct results?
   a) predicting how house prices will change in the next year
   b) predicting the weather for next month
   c) predicting the likely performance of the stock market next month
   d) predicting the temperature fall of a cup of coffee in a room

Score .... /5

Q **Answer all parts of all questions.**

1 State two factors that are likely to make a computer model unreliable.

.... (2 marks)

2 Give three reasons why a simulation might be used to investigate a situation instead of using real-life activity.

.... (3 marks)

3 Explain how a simulation can help a customer choose shelving in a do-it-yourself store.

.... (2 marks)

4 A model is constructed to predict cooking times for different-sized cakes at different temperatures. State two items of information that must be input into the model.

.... (2 marks)

5 What is the difference between a simulation and a model?

.... (2 marks)

Score .... /11

E This is an exam-style question. Answer all parts of the question.

Karen wants to improve her kitchen. She wants to redecorate it and also to install new units. She first sets up a model on her computer with a spreadsheet. She uses this to work out how much paint she will need.

1 What rules must Karen set up in the spreadsheet?

.... (2 marks)

2 What input is needed so that the model can produce the final costs?

.... (2 marks)

3 Karen decides that she will employ a decorator to do the work. The decorator charges by the hour. What further data does the model need in order to calculate the final cost?

.... (2 marks)

4 The shop that sells the kitchen units has a computer simulation so that customers can try out all their products before they buy.

a) Give three actions that the simulation software should be able to carry out.

....

.... (3 marks)

b) Give three items of data that Karen will have to provide to the simulation in order to get the results she wants.

....

.... (3 marks)

c) Give three items of data that the simulation system must already have available to it in order to work with Karen's requirements.

....

.... (3 marks)

Score .... /15

TOTAL SCORE   /31

For more help on this topic see KS3 ICT Success Guide pages 58–59

M Choose just one answer, a, b, c or d.

1 The hardware device that converts physical energy into electrical signals is called
a) an A-D converter b) a D-A converter
c) a sensor d) an interface.

2 Data from a data-logging session can best be sent to a spreadsheet for analysis in which format?
a) csv b) mp3
c) jpg d) rtf

3 A data-logging survey is monitoring the flow rate of a river over the course of a year. Which of these is a suitable logging interval?
a) 1 minute b) 1 hour
c) 1 week d) 1 month

4 Data collected in data-logging can usually be continuous – that is, any value between a maximum and a minimum. For example, the UK air temperature in summer can be anything between about 10°C and 35°C. Continuously varying data like this is called
a) digital b) analogue
c) discrete d) on-off.

5 The heating up of a cold room when the central heating is put on is being logged. A suitable logging period is
a) 1 tenth of a second
b) 1 minute
c) 1 hour
d) 1 day.

Score .... /5

Q Answer all parts of all questions.

1 A baker wants to monitor the efficiency of the insulation in his ovens.

a) What type of sensor would he need? .... (1 mark)

b) Suggest a suitable logging interval. .... (1 mark)

c) Suggest a suitable logging period. .... (1 mark)

2 What type of sensor is needed when

a) a scientist is logging the neutralisation of an acid? .... (1 mark)

b) a robot is placing items on a shelf in a warehouse? .... (1 mark)

c) a car park barrier is counting the cars that pass through? .... (1 mark)

3 a) Give two ways that software can present data from data-logging in an easy to understand way. .... (2 marks)

b) State what type of common software is usually the most suitable for processing data-logging results. .... (1 mark)

4 Give three reasons why data-logging can be better than taking physical readings manually.

.... (3 marks)

Score .... /12

58

This is an exam-style question. Answer all parts of the question.

Dave has a taxi company. His cars have data-logging equipment built into them.
There are sensors that log
- the number of wheel revolutions
- the oil pressure
- the engine water temperature
- the location of the taxi using GPS (global positioning system).

1 a) Give two reasons why logging the number of wheel revolutions would be useful to Dave.

....

.... (2 marks)

b) How could the data from the wheel revolutions be stored on board the taxi?

.... (1 mark)

c) Suggest a suitable logging interval for the wheel revolutions sensor.

.... (1 mark)

d) The data is later downloaded to a PC. What reasons could Dave have for doing this?

.... (2 marks)

2 a) The data from the engine sensors is stored on board each car.
Describe how this can help technicians when they service the car.

.... (2 marks)

b) Describe why car manufacturers prefer to install data-logging equipment to monitor conditions such as oil pressure instead of simply supplying a pressure gauge.

.... (2 marks)

c) Give two reasons why monitoring engines with sensors can be a disadvantage to the car owner.

....

.... (2 marks)

3 a) Data-logging can be useful in the design and development of car airbags.
Describe two physical events that could usefully be monitored in this case.

....

.... (2 marks)

b) Explain why data-logging is better than manual measurements in this case.

.... (2 marks)

Score .... /16

TOTAL SCORE   /33

For more help on this topic see KS3 ICT Success Guide pages 60–61

PROGRAMMING AND CONTROL

M Choose just one answer, a, b, c or d.

1 In a domestic appliance such as a washing machine, the instructions to the device are stored
  a) on a ROM chip   b) on a floppy disk
  c) in RAM   d) on a CD.

2 A small self-contained section of a computer program is called a
  a) file   b) module
  c) loop   d) branch.

3 A logo procedure is written with the following line in it:
  REPEAT 5 [FORWARD 50 RIGHT 360/5]
  This will draw
  a) a star   b) a triangle
  c) a curve   d) a pentagon.

4 Which of these is a programming language?
  a) FTP   b) HTML
  c) C++   d) DNS

5 Buttons are commonly seen on computer screens. A button is an example of
  a) an object   b) an application
  c) a utility   d) a driver.

Score .... /5

Q Answer all parts of all questions.

1 a) Give two reasons why computer programs are written in small pieces, then put together.

.... (2 marks)

b) Give two names that are used to describe a small self-contained piece of program code.

.... (2 marks)

2 Give three reasons why computers are so often used to control devices and machinery.

.... (3 marks)

3 A device that sprays paint on cars during manufacture is a robot, but an electric iron is not. What makes a robot different from other devices?

.... (2 marks)

4 What is a computer program?

.... (2 marks)

5 List three items that you might find in the home that can be computer controlled.

.... (3 marks)

Score .... /14

This is an exam-style question. Answer all parts of the question.

A small hotel has a lift that serves floors 1, 2 and 3.
It is controlled by a program on a microchip.

1 Why is a microchip used to control the lift instead of a full-sized computer?

.... (2 marks)

2 The manufacturers write a simple control program to operate the lift. One procedure from the program is given here:

(the symbol <> means 'does not equal')

procedure button_pressed

if button_on_floor_1 is pressed then floor_no=1
if button_on_floor_2 is pressed then floor_no=2
if button_on_floor_3 is pressed then floor_no=3
floor_at=detect_floor
if lift NOT moving AND floor_at <> floor_no then move_to(floor_no)

end procedure

a) This procedure relies on two other procedures to work. They are written elsewhere, but this procedure can call them.
   What are these two other procedures?

   .... (2 marks)

b) This procedure makes use of variables. These can temporarily hold data.
   Name two variables used by this procedure.

   .... (2 marks)

c) This procedure only runs if a certain event happens. What event will cause this procedure to run?

   .... (1 mark)

d) What happens if someone presses the button on floor 3 and the lift is already at floor 3?

   .... (1 mark)

e) What happens if the lift is moving and someone presses a button on any floor?

   .... (1 mark)

f) What happens if the lift is stationary at floor 3 and someone presses the button on floor 2?

   .... (1 mark)

Score .... /10

TOTAL SCORE   /29

For more help on this topic see KS3 ICT Success Guide pages 62–63

MULTIMEDIA

M Choose just one answer, a, b, c or d.

1 Which of these is a type of image compression?
   a) jpeg   b) mp3
   c) bmp   d) pdf

2 An image is stored on a computer system. Which of these image file types would take the greatest disk space?
   a) jpeg   b) gif
   c) zip   d) bmp

3 Which of these is an advantage of compressing an image file?
   a) it increases the resolution
   b) it improves the clarity
   c) it reduces download times
   d) it improves its quality when enlarged

4 Which of these is a disadvantage of using compressed files?
   a) they take longer to download
   b) they take up more disk space
   c) they take time to reconstruct
   d) they cannot be edited

5 Multimedia displays are often more effective than book-based training because
   a) they are interactive
   b) they are in colour
   c) they can use a variety of fonts
   d) they are up-to-date.

Score .... /5

Q Answer all parts of all questions.

1 State three different media that might make up a multimedia presentation.

.... (3 marks)

2 Explain why multimedia displays are more common than they used to be.

.... (2 marks)

3 Most business presentations are now produced with multimedia software. Explain why this is so popular.

.... (2 marks)

4 Explain why the development of DVDs has made multimedia more widely used.

.... (3 marks)

5 How might you use a multimedia encyclopaedia differently from a book–based encyclopaedia?

.... (2 marks)

Score .... /12

This is an exam-style question. Answer all parts of the question.

Joanne is a biology teacher. She wants to prepare a lesson about the blood circulation. She wants to make it more interesting than just drawing diagrams on the board. She decides to use multimedia techniques.

1   Give two examples of material that she could show her class with multimedia that she could not do with just a whiteboard.

....

.... (2 marks)

2   What equipment can be replaced by having a multimedia computer system?

....

.... (2 marks)

3   Give three examples of sources that Joanne could use in order to find material for her multimedia demonstration.

....

....

.... (3 marks)

4   Explain why making this presentation could cause legal problems.

....

.... (2 marks)

5   Why is Joanne keen to use multimedia to help with her lesson?

....

.... (2 marks)

6   Describe two ways in which Joanne could make the presentation easily visible to her class.

....

.... (2 marks)

Score .... /13

TOTAL SCORE   /30

M Choose just one answer, a, b, c or d.

1 A slide which contains material that is automatically displayed on all other slides is called a
   a) style slide   b) master slide
   c) template slide   d) background slide.

2 The effects that are displayed when moving from one slide to the next in a presentation are called
   a) templates   b) action settings
   c) transitions   d) layouts.

3 The slide sorter in a presentation can be used to
   a) design a slide
   b) change the order of slides
   c) create a background
   d) change the layout of a slide.

4 Which of these is the best advice when designing a slide show to present the year's sales figures to management?
   a) use lots of fonts
   b) use plenty of contrasting colours
   c) have animations on every page
   d) have a consistent design throughout the show

5 A self-running slide show would be most useful
   a) to show a school's activities on an open day
   b) to illustrate a presentation given by a speaker about a new product
   c) to help a teacher present a new topic to a class
   d) to accompany a candidate's presentation at a job interview.

Score ……. /5

Q Answer all parts of all questions.

1 A manager wants to explain a new marketing strategy to her sales staff. Give three reasons why a slide presentation would help.

   .... (3 marks)

2 Give three rules that can help to produce slides that are easy for the audience to follow.

   .... (3 marks)

3 Explain what is meant by a house style.

   .... (2 marks)

4 Explain how a template can help to make a slide show consistent.

   .... (2 marks)

5 What type of presentation is most likely to require timings to be set?

   .... (1 mark)

Score ……. /11

E This is an exam-style question. Answer all parts of the question.

Kevin is the manager of a branch of a Supermarket. He wants to install big screens around the store. These screens are to be connected to a computer running presentation software. Kevin wants to tell shoppers about special promotions as they walk around the store.

1 Why, in this case, is sound an important part of the presentation?

.... (1 mark)

2 The presentation will make considerable use of movie clips.
   a) Why is this more important in this case than in a presentation made to a
       seated audience?

   .... (2 marks)

   b) What will this heavy use of movie clips mean for the computer systems used?

   .... (2 marks)

After a month, Kevin has to make a presentation to the board to explain whether the idea of big screens has been a success. He makes a presentation to show them.

3 a) Give three ways that this presentation will differ in style from the one used in
       the supermarkets.

   .... (3 marks)

   b) Kevin wants to have the company logo on every slide. Explain how he can do this
       without manually inserting it on every slide.

   .... (2 marks)

   c) When Kevin has put the presentation together, he wants to change the order of
       some of the slides. Explain how he can do this.

   .... (2 marks)

   d) Kevin arranges his main points as bulleted lists. He makes each point fly in from
       the left when he clicks the mouse. Why is this a good technique?

   .... (2 marks)

Score .... /14

TOTAL SCORE   /30

For more help on this topic see KS3 ICT Success Guide pages 68–69

NETWORKS

M Choose just one answer, a, b, c or d.

1 A network confined to one site in a business is called
a) a LAN　　　　b) a WAN
c) a MAN　　　　d) an intranet.

2 Which of these components can be used to link the cables from lots of computers to a server?
a) a switch
b) a client machine
c) a network interface card
d) a router

3 Which of these network operating tasks is most likely to be done every day?
a) setting up new users
b) setting access rights
c) configuring the network printer
d) making backups

4 Which of these is the most likely reason that a small business would want a network instead of having lots of stand-alone computers?
a) it is cheaper
b) it can cut down on the number of IT staff needed
c) it makes it easier to share resources
d) it is less likely to have running problems

5 A client machine is another name for a
a) server　　　　b) router
c) workstation　　d) hub.

Score .... /5

Q Answer all parts of all questions.

1 Explain how a network can lead to reduced costs when purchasing expensive printers.

.... (2 marks)

2 Name three jobs that are carried out by servers on a computer network.

.... (3 marks)

3 Describe two ways in which the devices on a network can be connected together.

.... (2 marks)

4 What is a router for?

.... (2 marks)

5 Explain why networks can often be very expensive to maintain.

.... (2 marks)

Score .... /11

E This is an exam-style question. Answer all parts of the question.

Sarah is a dentist. She is very popular because she is willing to spend time with her patients explaining their problems and their treatment. She needs a partner to cope with the work. She also employs a dental hygienist who works in a separate room and a receptionist who keeps the patient records and prepares the bills on a stand-alone computer. Sarah wants to install a computer network to replace the stand-alone machine.

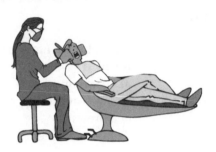

1   Explain how a network could help Sarah to deal with her patients more quickly.

.... (2 marks)

2   Explain how a network can help the two dentists and the hygienist work more effectively.

.... (2 marks)

3   What hardware will have to be installed on each computer in the network to allow them to communicate?

.... (1 mark)

4   Will Sarah's network be a LAN or a WAN? Explain why.

.... (2 marks)

5   Sarah and the other staff have to log in before they can use the new network.
    Give two reasons for this.

.... (2 marks)

6   Sarah wants to connect the network to the Internet so that she can send e-mails.
    a) What extra hardware is needed to allow this?

.... (1 mark)

    b) Explain two reasons why connecting the network to the Internet may cause problems for the dental practice.

.... (4 marks)

7   Sarah has to pay for more than just the hardware and software to set up and run her network. What additional costs are involved?

.... (2 marks)

Score .... /16

TOTAL SCORE   /32

For more help on this topic see KS3 ICT Success Guide pages 70–71

THE INTERNET

M Choose just one answer, a, b, c or d.

1 A protocol is
a) the language used to write programs on a web page
b) the speed of data transmission on a network
c) the rules that govern how computers communicate
d) the settings on a router.

2 When files are copied from a PC to a web server, which of these is used?
a) FTP   b) HTTP
c) SMP   d) POP

3 Which of these activities on the Internet would benefit most from having a broadband connection?
a) sending text-only e-mails
b) reading an article online
c) video conferencing
d) using a search engine

4 The software needed to display a web page is called
a) an editor
b) a web authoring package
c) a browser
d) an e-mail client.

5 Web pages have special symbols embedded in them that affect how the text is displayed. These markers are called
a) codes
b) tags
c) markers
d) controls.

Score .... /5

Q Answer all parts of all questions.

1 What are the three main services provided by the Internet?

.... (3 marks)

2 What is a computer called that provides web pages that can be viewed by surfers?

.... (1 mark)

3 a) What is meant by broadband?

.... (2 marks)

b) What type of signals are carried by broadband connections?

.... (1 mark)

c) What is ADSL and why is this a suitable broadband connection for a home user?

.... (2 marks)

4 What is hypertext?

.... (2 marks)

Score .... /11

E This is an exam-style question. Answer all parts of the question.

Riverside Pet Stores is setting up a website.

Here is the HTML code for it

```
<html>

<head>
<meta http-equiv="Content-Language" content="en-gb">
<meta http-equiv="Content-Type" content="text/html; charset=windows-1252">
<meta name="GENERATOR" content="Microsoft FrontPage 4.0">
<meta name="ProgId" content="FrontPage.Editor.Document">
<title>Riverside Pet Stores</title>
<meta name="Microsoft Theme" content="blends 011">
</head>

<body>

<h1 align="center">Riverside Pet Stores</h1>
<p align="center"><a href="http://page2.htm"><img border="0" src="cleo.jpg" width="199" height="195"></a></p>
<p align="center">Everything you need for happy pets</p>
<p align="center">Click on the <a href="http://page2.htm">cat</a> to enter site</p>

</body>

</html>
```

1 Some of the text is placed between <h1> and </h1>. What effect does this have?

.... (2 marks)

2 a) There are two hyperlinks on this web page. Identify them.

.... (2 marks)

b) When either of these hyperlinks is clicked, which page will the user be taken to?

.... (1 mark)

3 What protocol is used for transmitting this web page?

.... (1 mark)

4 What is the web address of this website?

.... (1 mark)

5 Riverside Pet Stores wants to provide some pages with lots of images to show all the products that they sell being used by animals.
a) Why might this be an annoyance to some users?

.... (2 marks)

b) Other users will not find lots of images a problem. Why are they not affected?

.... (2 marks)

Score .... /11

TOTAL SCORE   /27

For more help on this topic see KS3 ICT Success Guide pages 72–73

E-MAIL

M Choose just one answer, a, b, c or d.

1 Which of these is the best way to deal with spam?
a) send an e-mail back to the sender to complain
b) install a firewall
c) check it and delete it if it looks like spam
d) delete it without opening

2 Some e-mails can copy a program onto your computer that is disguised as something else and might spy on your activities. This program is called a
a) virus   b) worm
c) Trojan horse   d) cookie.

3 The main advantage of web-based e-mail over client-based e-mail is
a) it works more quickly
b) it lets you send bigger attachments
c) it can be accessed from any computer connected to the Internet
d) it is more secure.

4 Which of these is an advantage of using e-mail instead of ordinary mail?
a) e-mail is more secure
b) you can always rely on e-mail being read
c) you can always rely on e-mail reaching its destination
d) you can attach computer files to e-mails

5 If you send an e-mail to one person and want a copy to go to another person, you can add the extra address to
a) the subject box
b) the cc box
c) the body of the message
d) the address book.

Score .... /5

Q Answer all parts of all questions.

1 a) Give two advantages of using e-mail software based on your own computer over using web-based e-mail.

.... (2 marks)

b) Give two advantages of using web-based e-mail over e-mail software based on your own computer.

.... (2 marks)

2 a) What is spam? .... (2 marks)

b) What is the likely result of replying to spam?
Explain the reason for this. .... (2 marks)

3 Some websites include small programs that run on your computer.

a) What are these programs called? .... (1 mark)

Q Continued

b) How might a car manufacturer use these small programs to help advertise cars?

.... (2 marks)

4 State two common 'extras' that often come with web-based e-mail services.

.... (2 marks)

Score .... /13

E This is an exam-style question. Answer all parts of the question.

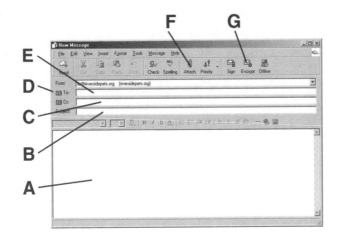

This is a typical screen used for setting up and sending an e-mail. It is set up so that Liz can send e-mails from work.

1 Give the letter that indicates the box where the recipient's e-mail address will go. .... (1 mark)

2 What will happen if someone clicks on the icon labelled D? .... (1 mark)

3 What reason might someone have for clicking on the button labelled G? .... (1 mark)

4 What would go into the box labelled C? .... (1 mark)

5 Where does the user type the e-mail message? .... (1 mark)

6 Which part of the e-mail will help the recipient to decide quickly if the e-mail needs urgent attention? .... (1 mark)

7 What is the purpose of the button labelled F? .... (1 mark)

8 Give two reasons why Liz should not use web-based e-mail for work communications.

.... (2 marks)

Score .... /9

TOTAL SCORE   /27

For more help on this topic see KS3 ICT Success Guide pages 74–75

NOTES